The *Speedy* Revision Guide

Key Stage 3
Tier 5–7

Introduction

 This revision guide is aimed at Tier 5–7 of the KS3 National Tests for Mathematics. It's the perfect size to keep with you at all times during the crucial weeks before the tests.

There is *speedy* coverage of each topic in the four main strands:
- Number
- Algebra
- Shape, space & measures
- Handling data

Everything you need to know about a topic is given on one or two pages, in the same format:
- **Essential facts**
  Everything you need to know, complete with examples.
- **Q & A**
  Easy-to-follow worked examples with clearly explained methods.
- **Check-up TESTs**
  To make sure everything has sunk in. (If you can do all the tests, you are heading in the right direction!)

On pages 72–73 there is a *speedy* revision test to check that you have remembered all the basic facts. (If you're short of time, try the revision test first, then revise those topics you got wrong; that truly is *speedy* revision!)

Good luck in your tests!

Contents

Special numbers

● Even and odd numbers

Even numbers end in 0, 2, 4, 6 or 8 and are exactly divisible by 2.
All other numbers are odd numbers – they end in 1, 3, 5, 7 or 9.

● Square numbers

Square numbers are whole numbers multiplied by themselves.

> ➤ **Example**
> '3 squared' is 3 × 3 = 9.
> '3 squared' is written 3^2.

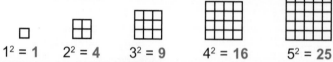

$1^2 = 1$ $2^2 = 4$ $3^2 = 9$ $4^2 = 16$ $5^2 = 25$

● Triangular numbers

Start at 1 and add 2, then 3, then 4, ...

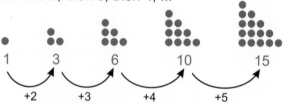

1   3   6   10   15

+2   +3   +4   +5

● Prime numbers

A prime number has exactly two factors (itself and 1).

Note: 1 is not a prime number (it has only one factor – itself).

You should memorise the first few primes: 2, 3, 5, 7, 11, 13, 17, ...
Apart from 2, primes are always odd numbers.
Any odd number that's in a times-table other than its own is not a prime number. e.g. 9 is not prime as it's in the 3 times-table.

---

1 Write down the first ten
   a even **b** odd **c** square **d** triangular numbers.
2 32, 49, 17, 21, 36, 3, 64
   From the list, write down the
   a even **b** odd **c** square **d** triangular **e** prime numbers.

TEST

Multiples, factors & prime factors

● Multiples

The <u>multiples</u> of a number are the numbers in its <u>times-table</u>.

➤ Example

The 3 times-table is:

$1 \times 3 = 3$, $2 \times 3 = 6$, $3 \times 3 = 9$ ...

The multiples of 3 are: 3, 6, 9, ...

● Factors

The <u>factors</u> of a number are the numbers that <u>divide into it exactly</u> (including 1 and itself).

You can use these tests to find out the factors of a number:

If it is <u>even</u>, then <u>2 is a factor</u>. (Even numbers end in 0, 2, 4, 6 or 8.)

If the <u>sum of the digits</u> is a <u>multiple of 3</u>, then <u>3 is a factor</u>.

If the <u>sum of the digits</u> is a <u>multiple of 9</u>, then <u>9 is a factor</u>.

If <u>half</u> the number is an <u>even number</u>, then <u>4 is a factor</u>.

If it <u>ends in 0 or 5</u>, then <u>5 is a factor</u>.

If it <u>ends in 0</u>, then <u>10 is a factor</u>.

➤ Q & A

Are 2, 3, 4, 5 and 10 factors of 310?

Answer

310 ends in 0, so <u>2, 5 and 10 are factors</u>.

$3 + 1 + 0 = 4$ which is not a multiple of 3, so <u>3 is not a factor</u>.

Half 310 = 155 which is odd, so <u>4 is not a factor</u>.

● Prime factors

Prime numbers that are factors of a number are called <u>prime factors</u>. For example, 3 is a prime factor of 15 (3 is prime and a factor of 15). You can write any number as a <u>product of its prime factors</u>:

> $20 = 4 \times 5 = 2 \times 2 \times 5 = 2^2 \times 5$

Break 20 into 4 × 5.

Break 4 into 2 × 2.

Only primes left. Rewrite the answer with indices.

---

1 List the first five multiples of these: **a** 5 **b** 8 **c** 6 **d** 9
2 List all the factors of these: **a** 8 **b** 32 **c** 40
3 Write these as products of their prime factors: **a** 36 **b** 84

TEST

LCM & HCF

● Least common multiple

The least common multiple (LCM) is the smallest number that is a multiple of all the numbers in question.

▶ Q & A

What is the LCM of 4 and 14?

▶ Method

❶ List the multiples of both numbers.
❷ Pick out the smallest number that's in both lists.

Answer

List the multiples of the numbers:
Multiples of 4 are 4, 8, 12, 16, 20, 24, 28, 32, ...
Multiples of 14 are 14, 28, 42, ...

The smallest number that's in both lists is 28,
so 28 is the LCM of 4 and 14.

Note: 'least common multiple' is the same thing as 'lowest common multiple'. Some people prefer lowest, some least – luckily they both shorten to LCM.

● Highest common factor

The highest common factor (HCF) is the largest number that is a factor of all the numbers in question.

▶ Q & A

What is the HCF of 24 and 36?

▶ Method

❶ List the factors of both numbers.
❷ Pick out the largest number that's in both lists.

Answer

List the factors of the numbers:
Factors of 24 are 1, 2, 3, 4, 6, 8, 12, 24
Factors of 36 are 1, 2, 3, 4, 6, 9, 12, 18, 36

The largest number that's in both lists is 12,
so 12 is the HCF of 24 and 36.

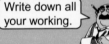
Write down all your working.

TEST

1 What is the LCM of **a** 6 and 8 **b** 16 and 36?
2 What is the HCF of **a** 4 and 16 **b** 21 and 35?

Speedy Revision

Multiplying & dividing by 10, 100, 1000, ...

● Multiplying by 10, 100 or 1000

	Th	H	T	U
			3	7

To multiply by:

10 move the digits <u>1 place left</u>   37 × 10 = **3 7 0**

100 move the digits <u>2 places left</u>   37 × 100 = **3 7 0 0**

1000 move the digits <u>3 places left</u>   37 × 1000 = **3 7 0 0 0**

● Dividing by 10, 100 or 1000

	Th	H	T	U
	4	0	0	0

To divide by:

10 move the digits <u>1 place right</u>   4000 ÷ 10 = **4 0 0**

100 move the digits <u>2 places right</u>   4000 ÷ 100 = **4 0**

1000 move the digits <u>3 places right</u>   4000 ÷ 1000 = **4**

You can apply the above methods to <u>decimals</u>. You can also extend to multiplying and dividing by <u>multiples</u> such as 40, 300 and 7000.

▶ Q & A

Work out: **a** 1.8 × 100 **b** 1.8 ÷ 0.1 **c** 12 × 300 **d** 160 ÷ 40

Answer

a Multiplying by 100 so move the digits
2 places to the left: 1.8 × 100 = <u>180</u>

> 10 is the <u>reciprocal</u> of 0.1: $10 = \frac{1}{0.1}$

b Dividing by 0.1 is the same as multiplying by 10 so
move the digits 1 place to the left: 1.8 × 10 = <u>18</u>

c To multiply by 300, first multiply by 3 and then multiply by 100:
12 × 3 = 36; 36 × 100 = <u>3600</u> (move digits 2 places left).

d To divide by 40, first divide by 4 and then divide by 10:
160 ÷ 4 = 40; 40 ÷ 10 = <u>4</u> (move digits 1 place right).

1 a 39 × 10   **b** 8 × 1000   **c** 7.1 × 0.1 **d** 1.5 × 100
   e 420 ÷ 10   **f** 6400 ÷ 100 **g** 16.3 ÷ 0.1 **h** 149 ÷ 0.01
2 a 2.4 × 1000 **b** 2.4 ÷ 100   **c** 21 × 4000 **d** 210 ÷ 300

TEST

Rounding (1)

● Rounding to the nearest ten

❶ Focus on the tens digit.

$$37\overset{\downarrow}{2}\underset{\uparrow}{1}.6 \quad ⟹ \quad 3720$$

❷ If the number to the right of the tens digit (i.e. the units) is 5 or more, round up. Otherwise the tens digit stays the same.

❸ Get rid of everything to the right of the tens column. Remember to put a zero as a place holder in the units column.

● Rounding to the nearest hundred, thousand, ...

Do this the same way as rounding to the nearest ten, but focus on the hundreds or thousands digit.

> ➤ **Example**
> 3721.6 → 3700 to nearest 100
> 3721.6 → 4000 to nearest 1000

● Rounding to decimal places

'Decimal place' is often abbreviated to 'dp' or 'd.p.'.

When rounding to 1 dp focus on the 1st digit after the decimal point. For 2 dp, 3 dp, ... focus on the 2nd, 3rd, ... digit after the decimal point.

➤ **Q & A**

Round 0.168 to 2 dp.

Answer

Focus on the 2nd decimal place.

$$0.16\underset{\nwarrow}{8} \quad ⟹ \quad 0.17$$

8 is '5 or more', so round 6 up to 7.

➤ **Method** (rounding to 2 dp)

❶ Focus on the 2nd dp.
❷ If the digit to the right of the 2nd dp is 5 or more, round upwards. Otherwise the 2nd dp stays the same.
❸ Get rid of everything to the right of the 2nd dp.

Rounding (2)

● Rounding to significant figures

The 1st significant figure is the 1st non-zero digit from the left.

The 2nd, 3rd, ... significant figures are the digits immediately after the 1st significant figure, even if they are zeros.

'Significant figures' is often shortened to 'sig figs', 'sig. figs.', 'sf' or 's.f.'.

> **► Example**
>
>   1st 2nd 3rd 4th
>
> **0 . 0 5 0 9 6**

► Q & A

Round 5384 to 2 sig figs.

Answer

Focus on the 2nd sig fig.

5384 ⟹ 5400

8 is '5 or more', so round upwards.

Add zeros. (It would be silly to round to 54.)

> **► Method** (rounding to 2 sf)
>
> ❶ Focus on the 2nd sig fig.
> ❷ If the digit to the right of the 2nd sig fig is 5 or more, round upwards. Otherwise the 2nd sig fig stays the same.
> ❸ Get rid of everything to the right of the 2nd sig fig. (Add zeros as place holders if needed.)

● Some extra rounding examples

Make sure you can see how these were rounded.

	to 1 dp	to 2 dp	to 3 dp	to 1 sf	to 2 sf	to 3 sf
24.9374	24.9	24.94	24.937	20	25	24.9
0.9527	1.0	0.95	0.953	1	0.95	0.953
0.07457	0.1	0.07	0.075	0.07	0.075	0.0746
888.8888	888.9	888.89	888.889	900	890	889

---

1 Round these to the nearest hundred: 27 920, 2875, 62

2 Round these to 2 dp: 0.582, 0.019, 12.882

3 Round these to 2 sf: 352, 1.006, 0.809

4 Estimate the answers to these by first rounding all numbers to 1 sf: **a** $\dfrac{(5.45 + 10.85)}{2.86}$ **b** $\dfrac{(989 \times 304)}{296}$

TEST

Fractions (1)

A fraction shows the number of parts out of the whole.

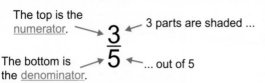

The top is the <u>numerator</u>. → $\frac{3}{5}$ ← 3 parts are shaded ...

The bottom is the <u>denominator</u>. → ... out of 5

➤ Example
$\frac{3}{5}$ is three-fifths.

$\frac{3}{5}$ means 3 out of 5.

● Equivalent fractions

You can find <u>equivalent fractions</u> by <u>multiplying/dividing</u> top and bottom by the <u>same number</u>.

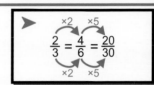

$$\frac{2}{3} = \frac{4}{6} = \frac{20}{30}$$
×2 ×5

● Simplifying fractions

To write a fraction in its simplest form <u>divide</u> <u>numerator and denominator</u> (top and bottom) by the <u>highest common factor</u>.

This is often called '<u>cancelling</u>'.

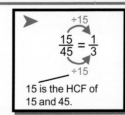

$$\frac{15}{45} = \frac{1}{3}$$
÷15

15 is the HCF of 15 and 45.

● Adding/subtracting fractions

You can only add/subtract fractions once they have the <u>same denominator</u>.

➤ $\frac{2}{3} + \frac{1}{5} = \frac{10}{15} + \frac{3}{15} = \frac{10 + 3}{15} = \frac{13}{15}$

● Improper & mixed fractions

<u>Improper fractions</u> are '<u>top heavy</u>', i.e. the numerator is bigger than the denominator.
<u>Mixed numbers</u> are made up of a <u>whole number</u> and a <u>fraction</u>.

➤ $\frac{8}{5}$ is an improper fraction.
$3\frac{3}{5}$ is a mixed number.

---

1 Write down the fraction that is shaded:

2 Write as a fraction in its simplest form: **a** $\frac{4}{6}$ **b** $\frac{12}{16}$ **c** 4p out of 10p

3 Work out **a** $\frac{2}{9} + \frac{2}{3}$ **b** $\frac{3}{4} - \frac{5}{8}$.

4 Write $1\frac{2}{3}$ as an improper fraction.

5 Write $\frac{10}{3}$ as a mixed number.

TEST

Fractions (2)

● Multiplying fractions

You multiply the numerators, then you multiply the denominators.

> ### Example
>
> $$\frac{3}{4} \times \frac{5}{7} = \frac{3 \times 5}{4 \times 7} = \frac{15}{28}$$

Sometimes you can cancel out common factors to make the multiplication easier:

> ### Example
>
> $$\frac{9}{10} \times \frac{15}{36} = \frac{\cancel{9}^{1}}{10} \times \frac{15}{\cancel{36}_{4}} = \frac{9}{\cancel{10}_{2}} \times \frac{\cancel{15}^{3}}{36} = \frac{1 \times 3}{2 \times 4} = \frac{3}{8}$$
>
> 9 is a common factor of 9 and 36, so you can cancel these out (there is 1 nine in 9 and 4 nines in 36).
>
> 5 is a common factor of 10 and 15, so you can cancel these out (there are 2 fives in 10 and 3 fives in 15).

● Dividing fractions

To divide fractions, you turn the second one over and then multiply.

> ### Example
>
> $$\frac{2}{9} \div \frac{3}{7} = \frac{2}{9} \times \frac{7}{3} = \frac{2 \times 7}{9 \times 3} = \frac{14}{27}$$

● Fraction of

To find one-third of something you divide by three.

To find two-thirds, you find a third then multiply by two.

You can find other fractions exactly the same way – find one part then multiply.

> ### Example
>
> $\frac{1}{3}$ of £60 = £60 ÷ 3 = £20
>
> $\downarrow$×2 $\qquad\qquad\qquad$ $\downarrow$×2
>
> $\frac{2}{3}$ of £60 = £20 × 2 = £40

● Fractions on your calculator

Your calculator should have a button that looks like **a**b/c.

To work out $\frac{2}{9} \div \frac{3}{7}$ press **2** **a**b/c **9** **÷** **3** **a**b/c **7** **=** to get

| `14⌐27` | in your display. This means the answer is $\frac{14}{27}$.

1 **a** $\frac{5}{7} \times \frac{2}{7}$ **b** $\frac{6}{8} \times \frac{8}{9}$ **c** $\frac{2}{9} \div \frac{2}{3}$ **d** $\frac{4}{7} \div \frac{8}{9}$ **e** Find $\frac{2}{5}$ of £55.

2 Check your answers to **Q1** on a calculator.

TEST

Percentages

● 'Per cent' means 'out of 100'

So '10 per cent' means '10 out of 100'.

$$10\% = \frac{10}{100} \text{ or } \frac{1}{10}$$

10%

The % symbol can be used in place of the words 'per cent'.

● Express a number as a percentage of another

➤ Q & A
Express £26 as a percentage of £40.

Answer
26 ÷ 40 = 0.65
0.65 × 100% = 65%

➤ Method
❶ Divide the first number by the second number.
❷ Multiply by 100%.

● Percentage of

➤ Q & A
Find 20% of £400.

Answer
1% is £400 ÷ 100 = £4
20% is £4 × 20 = £80

➤ Method
❶ Divide by 100 to find 1%.
❷ Multiply by the number of per cent required.

● Percentage increase/decrease

➤ Q & A
Increase £20 by 17.5%.

Answer
1% is £20 ÷ 100 = £0.20.
17.5% is £0.20 × 17.5 = £3.50
                    (this is the increase).
The answer is £20 + £3.50 = £23.50.

➤ Method
❶ Find the increase (or decrease).
❷ Add it to the price. (Take it off for a decrease.)

---

1 Express 12 kg as a percentage of 60 kg.
2 Find 35% of £120.
3 a Increase £1000 by 20%. b Decrease £200 by 5%.

TEST

Speedy Revision

Ratio & proportion (2)

➤ Q & A

It is 1.75 km to the shop and 2500 m to the library.

What is the ratio of the distances?

Answer

1.75 : 2.5   [in km]

175 : 250   [×100]

7 : 10   [÷25]

➤ Method

❶ Write the amounts in the same units.

❷ Write the two amounts without units as 'amount 1 : amount 2'.

❸ If necessary, multiply both sides by any big number to get rid of decimals/fractions.

❹ Divide by the HCF to simplify.

● Dividing in a given ratio

➤ Q & A

Divide £120 in the ratio 2 : 3.

Answer

2 + 3 = 5 parts

1 part is £120 ÷ 5 = £24

2 parts are £24 × 2 = £48

3 parts are £24 × 3 = £72

£48 : £72

➤ Method

❶ Add the ratio to find the total number of parts.

❷ Find the value of 1 part.

❸ Multiply by the number of parts on each side of the ratio.

● Solving problems

➤ Q & A

5 apples cost 90p.

How much would 8 apples cost?

Answer

5 apples cost: 90p

1 apple costs: 90p ÷ 5 = 18p

8 apples cost: 18p × 8 = 144p or £1.44

➤ Method

❶ Divide by 5 to find the cost of 1.

❷ Multiply by 8 to find the cost of 8.

---

1 Simplify: **a** 3 : 18   **b** 27 : 15   **c** 14 km : 120 m

2 Divide 800 ml in the ratio 3 : 7.

3 8 notebooks cost £3.60. How much will 15 cost?

TEST

Negative numbers

● Temperatures on a thermometer

Temperatures on a thermometer can be positive or negative.

Numbers <u>more than 0</u> are <u>positive numbers</u>.
e.g. 5, 10, ...
Numbers <u>less than 0</u> are <u>negative numbers</u>.
e.g. –5, –10, ...

–10°C is <u>less than</u> –5°C, as it is <u>lower down</u> the thermometer.
You can write this as –10 < –5.

Numbers getting bigger: temperatures getting hotter.

Numbers getting smaller: temperatures getting colder.

● Ordering negative numbers

You can order these:
–2, 3, 1, –4, 5
on a number line.

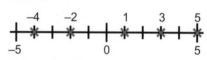

In order, smallest first: –4, –2, 1, 3, 5

● Adding & subtracting negative numbers

Count <u>on</u> when you <u>add</u>.

$$-3 + 5 = 2$$

Start at –3 and go on 5.

Count <u>back</u> when you <u>subtract</u>.

$$-1 - 7 = -8$$

Start at –1 and go back 7.

TEST

1 Look at the thermometer. Which is smaller, 5 or –10?
2 Put these in order, smallest first: 2, 0, –4, –5, 3
3 Show on a number line: **a** –8 + 3 **b** –2 – 3

Powers & roots (1)

● Powers

Powers are just a short way of writing repeated multiplication.

The 'power' or 'index' tells you how many times the number appears in the repeated multiplication.

➤ Example

$5^4 = 5 \times 5 \times 5 \times 5 = 625$

The power is 4, so 5 appears 4 times.

5^4 is '5 to the power of 4'.

● Special powers

Any non-zero number 'to the power of 0' is 1.

Any number 'to the power of 1' is itself.

➤ Examples

$1^0 = 1$, $2^0 = 1$, $9^0 = 1$

$1^1 = 1$, $2^1 = 2$, $5^1 = 5$

● Square and cube roots

Finding the root is the opposite (or inverse) of finding the power.

'What is the square root of 16?' means the same as 'What number squared is 16?'

➤ Example

$\sqrt{16} = 4$ or -4

as $4 \times 4 = 16$

and $-4 \times -4 = 16$

➤ Q & A

What is $\sqrt[3]{125}$?

Answer

This is the short way of writing 'What number is the cube root of 125?'

So ask yourself 'What number cubed is 125?'

The answer to this is 5:

$5 \times 5 \times 5 = 125$, so $\sqrt[3]{125} = 5$

➤ Method

❶ Check whether you are taking the square or cube root.

❷ Ask yourself what number squared/cubed gives the number in the question.

❸ Remember that square roots can be negative.

● Negative powers

A negative power is the reciprocal of a positive power.

('Reciprocal' just means 'one over'.)

➤ Examples

$10^{-3} = \frac{1}{10^3} = \frac{1}{1000} = 0.001$

$6^{-1} = \frac{1}{6^1} = \frac{1}{6}$

Powers & roots (2)

● Working with powers

◆ To multiply powers of the same number add the indices.

◆ To divide powers of the same number subtract the indices.

◆ To take the power of a power multiply the indices.

> ➤ **Examples**
>
> $4^2 \times 4^3 = 4^{2+3} = 4^5$
>
> $3^7 \div 3^4 = 3^{7-4} = 3^3$
>
> $(10^2)^6 = 10^{2 \times 6} = 10^{12}$

➤ **Q & A**   What is $12^9 \div 12^7$?

Answer

$12^9 \div 12^7 = 12^{9-7} = 12^2 = \underline{144}$

> ➤ **Method**
>
> ❶ Use the above rules to simplify the calculation.
>
> ❷ Evaluate the power.

● Fractional powers

These are just another way of showing roots. The denominator (bottom) of the fraction tells you which root to take.

> ➤
> $25^{\frac{1}{2}} = \sqrt{25} = 5$
>
> $8^{\frac{1}{3}} = \sqrt[3]{8} = 2$

● Powers & roots on your calculator

You should have some buttons like these on your calculator:

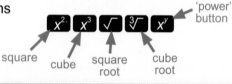

'power' button

square cube square root cube root

To work out $\sqrt{169}$, press [√] [1] [6] [9] [=]. On some calculators you press [√] after you enter the number, i.e. [1] [6] [9] [√].

Sometimes [√] is a '2nd function' written above [x^2]. If your calculator is like this you have to press [SHIFT] [x^2] [1] [6] [9] [=].

To work out 5^8, press [5] [x^y] [8] [=].

---

1 Find these powers: **a** 12^2 **b** 4^3 **c** 2^5 **d** 8^0 **e** 100^1 **f** 10^{-2}

2 Find these roots: **a** $\sqrt{36}$ **b** $\sqrt{64}$ **c** $\sqrt[3]{1000}$ **d** $27^{\frac{1}{3}}$

3 Combine these powers: **a** $7^4 \times 7^3$ **b** $2^{10} \div 2^5$ **c** $(5^8)^3$

Check your answers to questions **1** and **2** on your calculator.

TEST

Speedy Revision

Standard index form (1)

● Writing numbers in standard index form

Standard index form (sometimes just called standard form) is a short way of writing really small or large numbers.

The first number is always a number between 1 and 10. (It can be 1 but not 10.)

$$3 \times 10^9$$

The power of 10 tells you how far the decimal point has moved.

Written the long way, this number is 3 000 000 000.

➤ Q & A

Write these in standard form: **a** 36 000   **b** 0.0045

Answer

a The decimal point needs to move 4 places to get to a number between 1 and 10:

3 6000●

So, in standard form, the number is written as 3.6×10^4.

b The decimal point needs to move 3 places to get to a number between 1 and 10:

0●004●5

0.0045 is less than 1, so the power of 10 is negative.

So, in standard form, the number is written as 4.5×10^{-3}.

> If the original number is smaller than 1 then the power is negative.

● Changing back to normal numbers

➤ Q & A

Write 2.3×10^{-5} as a normal number.

Answer

As the power of 10 is negative we are dealing with a number less than 1, so the decimal point needs to move 5 places to the left:

Put extra zeros in.

0●00002●3

The answer is 0.000 023.

---

1 Write these numbers in standard index form:
  a 345   **b** 0.000 24   **c** 45 000   **d** 764 000 000
2 Write these as normal numbers: **a** 3.7×10^3 **b** 1.2×10^{-4}

TEST

Speedy Revision

19

Standard index form (2)

● Standard index form with a calculator

Your calculator will have a button that looks like one of these:
EXP **E** **EE** **×10ˣ**. This is the standard form button.

To enter a standard form number like 4.6×10^{11} into your calculator just press **4** **●** **6** **EXP** **1** **1** **=** and you'll get something like [4.6^{11}] on your display.

Written methods (1)

● Addition & subtraction

➤ Q & A

a $4.72 + 3.51$

Answer

a

$$
\begin{array}{r}
4.72 \\
+\,3.51 \\
\hline
8.23 \\
\end{array}
$$
₁

$7 + 5 = 12$
Carry the '1' to the units column.

b $57.3 - 1.28$

Answer

b

Add a zero place holder.

$$
\begin{array}{r}
57.3^{2}{}^{1}0 \\
-\ \ 1.28 \\
\hline
56.02 \\
\end{array}
$$

0 is less than 8 so 'borrow' from the next column.
$10 - 8 = 2$

➤ **Method**

❶ Line up the units.
❷ Add/subtract a column at a time, starting on the right.

● Multiplication

When multiplying decimals it is often easiest to ignore the decimal point(s) and then divide by an appropriate power of 10 (10, 100, ...).

➤ Example

To find 7.18×9, work out 718×9 then divide by 100.

100 because there are 2 digits after the decimal point in 7.18

$$
\begin{array}{r}
718 \\
\times\ \ \ 9 \\
\hline
\end{array}
$$

$700 \times 9 = 6300$
$10 \times 9 =\ \ \ 90$
$8 \times 9 = +\ \ 72$
$\overline{718 \times 9 = 6462}$ $\xrightarrow{\div 100}$ 64.62

Written methods (2)

● Division

Keep taking off multiples of the divisor (the number you're dividing by) until you can't subtract any more.

➤ Q & A

Work out 452 ÷ 6.

Answer

```
6 ) 452
   − 420    70 × 6
     32
   − 30     5 × 6
      2
```

2 < 6, so you can't take off any more 6s.

Sometimes you won't be able to get to zero, and you'll have to give a <u>remainder</u> as part of the answer.

Answer = 75 remainder 2

● Division with decimals

The method is the same as for whole numbers, but make sure you keep the decimal points lined up.

Write 70.0 rather than 70 to help you keep everything in columns.

There is no remainder this time.

➤ Example

105.7 ÷ 7

```
7 ) 105.7
   − 70.0    10 × 7
     35.7
   − 35.0    5 × 7
      0.7
   −  0.7    0.1 × 7
      0.0
```

Answer = <u>15.1</u>

You can convert a division by a decimal to division by a whole number by multiplying everything by 10, 100, 1000, etc.

For example, to work out 10.57 ÷ 0.7 you could work out 105.7 ÷ 7 instead.

● Estimating calculations

Always check answers to calculations by estimating.
For example, 7.18 × 9 is roughly 7 × 10 = 70.

So when you get the actual answer of 64.62, you can be confident you haven't made a ridiculous mistake.

Always make an estimate

Use written methods to calculate:
1 a 5.16 + 2.73   b 1.19 + 2.35   c 2.3 − 2.14   d 171.541 − 5.71
2 a 36 × 23   b 121 × 14   c 6.42 × 7
3 a 63.5 ÷ 5   b 120.6 ÷ 9   c 23.76 ÷ 1.1

TEST

Calculations with brackets

● Order of operations

When faced with something like $5^2 - 2 \times (7 - 3)$ you have to work out each part in the correct order, else you'll get the wrong answer. Always do operations in this order:

Brackets	$5^2 - 2 \times (7 - 3)$
Squares	$= 5^2 - 2 \times 4$
Divide and Multiply	$= 25 - 2 \times 4$
Add and Subtract	$= 25 - 8$
	$= 17$

You can remember the order of operations with the word **BIDMAS**. **B**rackets, then **I**ndices, **D**ivision, **M**ultiplication, **A**ddition, **S**ubtraction. ('Indices' is the fancy word for squares, cubes, etc.)

If there are several multiplications and divisions (or additions and subtractions) do them one at a time from <u>left to right</u>.

For example:	Not:
$24 \div 6 \div 2$	$24 \div 6 \div 2$
$= 4 \div 2$	$= 24 \div 3$
$= 2$ ✔	$= 8$ ✘

● Brackets on a calculator

Use the <u>bracket buttons</u>, **( )**, on your calculator <u>exactly where they appear</u> in a calculation. For $72 - (18 + 36)$ press:

7 **2** **−** **(** **1** **8** **+** **3** **6** **)** **=** to get 18.

Look out for <u>sneaky brackets</u>:

$\frac{16 - 10}{2}$ is really $(16 - 10) \div 2$, so you have to <u>use brackets</u>.

Press: **(** **1** **6** **−** **1** **0** **)** **÷** **2** **=** ✔

Not: **1** **6** **−** **1** **0** **÷** **2** **=** ✘

Work these out on paper. Check your answers on a calculator.
a $3 \times 5 - 2 \times 4$ **b** $2.8 \times (15 - 2)$ **c** $56 \div 4 \div 2$ **d** $\frac{28}{(11 + 3)}$

TEST

Speedy Revision

Tier 5

Using letters

In algebra, letters represent <u>unknown</u> <u>numbers</u> or numbers that can <u>change</u>.

$n - 1$ means <u>one less</u> than n
$n + 5$ means <u>five more</u> than n
$n + n$ means <u>two lots of n</u> or $2 \times n$

> ➤ **Example**
> Think of a number. I don't know what number you are thinking of, so I'll call it n.

● Terms and expressions

A <u>term</u> is some numbers and letters multiplied together.

$$4a + b + 3ab + 2$$

a term b term ab term   number term

A collection of terms like this is called an <u>expression</u>.

● Collecting like terms

$4a$ and $3a$ are <u>like terms</u> because they have the <u>same letters</u>.

$2a$ and $5b$ are <u>not like terms</u> because they have <u>different letters</u>.

You can <u>simplify</u> expressions by <u>collecting like terms</u>.

$$4a \quad + \quad 3a \quad = \quad 7a$$

'<u>4</u> lots of a' and '<u>3</u> lots of a' makes '<u>7</u> lots of a'.

● Algebraic fractions

Algebraic fractions are fractions with letters in such as $\frac{x}{5}$ or $\frac{2x+3}{3}$. They may look odd, but you just treat them as normal fractions.

➤ **Q & A**

Work out $\frac{x}{3} + \frac{4x}{3}$.

Answer

The denominators are the same, so it's just a case of adding the numerators: $\quad \frac{x}{3} + \frac{4x}{3} = \frac{x + 4x}{3} = \frac{5x}{3}$

---

1 Simplify these expressions by collecting like terms:
   a $t + t + t$ **b** $n + n + n + n$ **c** $y + 2y$ **d** $3x + 2 + x$

2 Add these fractions: **a** $\frac{2x}{5} + \frac{4x}{5}$ **b** $\frac{1}{d} + \frac{2}{d}$

TEST

Brackets

● Multiplying out single brackets

To <u>get rid of brackets</u> from an expression, you have to <u>multiply</u> everything <u>inside</u> the brackets by the term <u>outside</u>.
This is also called '<u>expanding brackets</u>'.

> The 3 multiplies the x and the 2.
>
> $$3(x + 2) = 3 \times x + 3 \times 2 = 3x + 6$$
>
> Outside   Inside
>
> $3(m - 4) = 3m - 12$ $x(y + z) = xy + xz$ $a(4a + b) = 4a^2 + ab$

If the term outside the brackets is <u>negative</u>, you have to <u>change the sign</u> of each term inside the brackets when you multiply out.

> $$-2(a + 3) = -2a - 6$$ $$-3(c - d) = -3c + 3d$$
>
> A plus becomes a minus.   A minus becomes a plus.

● Multiplying out double brackets

➤ Q & A

Simplify $(a + 3)(a - 2)$.

Answer

It doesn't need to be a work of art – just join each term in the first bracket to each term in the second.

$(a + 3)(a - 2)$

$= (a \times a) + (a \times -2) + (3 \times a) + (3 \times -2)$
Left eyebrow   Mouth   Nose   Right eyebrow

$= a^2 - 2a + 3a - 6$

$= a^2 + a - 6$

➤ Method

❶ <u>Draw a face</u> with two eyebrows, a nose and a mouth:

❷ <u>Multiply</u> together the terms that are <u>joined by lines</u>.

❸ Collect like terms together.

Multiply out these brackets:
a $4(x + 2)$ **b** $m(n + 7)$ **c** $a(a + b)$ **d** $-4(d - 5)$
e $(x + 2)(x + 3)$ **f** $(x + 2)(x - 5)$ **g** $(x + 1)^2$

TEST

Equations

● Equations

An <u>equation</u> shows that two expressions are <u>equal</u>, e.g. $2x + 4 = 3x$.

● Solving equations

Solving equations is about finding the <u>value of the unknown</u> letter.
You can <u>add</u>, <u>subtract</u>, <u>multiply</u> or <u>divide</u> both sides by the same
number, but you must do <u>exactly the same</u> thing <u>to both sides</u>.

➤ Q & A

Solve $7x - 4 = 10$ to find the value of x.

Answer

You need to end up with $x =$ something.

Get rid of the $- 4$ by
adding 4 to both sides.

$$7x - 4 = 10$$
$$7x - 4 + 4 = 10 + 4 \qquad \text{[+4 to \underline{both} sides]}$$
$$7x = 14$$

Get rid of the × 7 by
dividing both sides by 7
($7x$ means $x × 7$).

$$7x ÷ 7 = 14 ÷ 7 \qquad \text{[÷ \underline{both} sides by 7]}$$
$$\underline{x = 2}$$

● Two important examples

There are two further types of equations they could throw at you:

❶ <u>The equation contains brackets</u>, e.g. $2(x + 5) = 18$
The first thing to do is to <u>multiply out the brackets</u> (see previous page).
Here, the equation becomes $2x + 10 = 18$.
You then solve it as normal (like above **Q & A**, but -10 then $÷2$).

❷ <u>The unknown letter appears on both sides</u>, e.g. $5x = 2x + 6$
You need to get the <u>letters</u> on <u>one side</u> and <u>numbers</u> on the <u>other</u>.
In this case, subtract $2x$ from both sides to get $3x = 6$.
You then solve it as normal (try dividing both sides by 3 ...)

---

1 Solve these equations: **a** $2x + 5 = 11$ **b** $3x - 8 = 16$
2 Finish solving the 'Two important examples', then solve:
  a $4(2x + 3) = 28$ **b** $10x = 3x + 14$

TEST

Formulae & substitution

● Formulae

A <u>formula</u> is basically a rule that <u>turns one number into another</u>.

> ### ➤ Example

Jo has a machine that makes chocolate biscuits.
One packet of biscuit mix makes four biscuits.

You can write this as a formula in words:

<u>Number of biscuits = 4 × the number of packets of biscuit mix</u>

You can also write this with algebra as <u>B = 4P</u>,
where <u>B</u> represents <u>the number of biscuits</u> and <u>P</u> represents
<u>the number of packets of biscuit mix</u>.

● Substituting numbers into formulae & expressions

You can <u>substitute</u> a number into an <u>expression</u> to find its value.

To substitute $y = 3$ into $2y + 5$, just write '3' in place of 'y' then work out the answer.

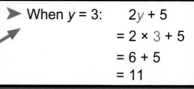

> ➤ When $y = 3$: $2y + 5$
> $= 2 × 3 + 5$
> $= 6 + 5$
> $= 11$

The trickiest substitution they could give you is one involving squares or cubes:

➤ Q & A

Given the formula $y = 4x^3$, find the value of y when $x = 2$.

Answer

Write out the formula again with 2 in the place of x:

$y = 4 × 2^3$
$= 4 × 2 × 2 × 2$ ◄── 2^3 means 2 times by itself 3 times
$= \underline{32}$ ◄── Double 4, then double again, then double again!

---

1 A plumber charges £25 per hour. Write a formula, in algebra, for the charge (C) in terms of number of hours worked (h).

2 Use your formula from **Q1** to work out the charge for 8 hours.

3 Work out the value of a when $b = 3$ in these formulae:
  a $a = 3b + 2$ **b** $a = 2b^2 + 1$

TEST

Rearranging formulae

Making x the <u>subject</u> of a <u>formula</u> means rewriting it as <u>$x = ...$</u>
The formula often has a power of the subject or the subject occurs twice.

● What to do with powers of the subject

➤ Q & A

Make x the subject of $y = 36x^2$.

Answer

$y = 36x^2$

$\sqrt{y} = 6x$ [square root]

$\dfrac{\sqrt{y}}{6} = x$ [÷6]

$x = \dfrac{\sqrt{y}}{6}$ [rewrite]

➤ Method

❶ If the <u>subject</u> has been squared, <u>square root both sides</u> of the equation. If the subject has been cubed, take the cube root.

❷ <u>Divide both sides</u> by the number now multiplying the subject.

❸ Rewrite the equation with the <u>subject on the left</u>.

● What to do if the subject occurs twice

➤ Q & A

Make x the subject of
$x + 6 = 3x + y$.

Answer

$x + 6 = 3x + y$

$6 = 2x + y$ [−x]

$2x + y = 6$ [rewrite]

$2x = 6 - y$ [−y]

$x = \dfrac{6 - y}{2}$ [÷2]

➤ Method

❶ Subtract the <u>smallest</u> subject term from both sides.

❷ <u>Rewrite</u> the equation with the remaining <u>subject</u> term <u>on the left</u> if necessary.

❸ <u>Add/subtract</u> any <u>non-subject terms</u> on the left to/from both sides.

❹ <u>Divide both sides</u> by the number now multiplying the subject.

---

1 Make q the subject of   **a** $p = 4q^2$ **b** $p = 81q^2$.
2 Make a the subject of   **a** $2a + 3b = a + 1$ **b** $a + 5b = 4a - b$.

TEST

Sequences & number patterns (1)

A <u>sequence</u> is a list of numbers that <u>follows</u> <u>a pattern</u> or rule.

> Each number in a sequence is called a <u>term</u>.
> 2, 4, 6, 8, ...
> ↖ 3rd term

● Adding or subtracting patterns

This is where a number is added or subtracted to get the next term in the sequence.

● Multiplying or dividing patterns

Here you multiply or divide to get the next term.

● Sequence diagrams

The trick is to convert the diagrams into a sequence of <u>numbers</u>.

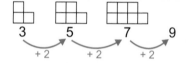

● *n*th term

The *n*th term is an expression used to find <u>any</u> term in a sequence.

> ### ➤ Example
>
> If someone tells you that the <u>*n*th</u> term of a sequence is <u>$3n + 4$</u>, then you can quickly work out any term in the sequence.
>
> The <u>1st</u> term is $3 \times \underline{1} + 4 = 7$, and the <u>100th</u> term is $3 \times \underline{100} + 4 = 304$.
>
> Just substitute the term number in place of *n*.

---

1 What is the next term in each of these sequences?
  a 5, 8, 11, 14, ... **b** 3, 6, 12, 24, ... **c** 21, 17, 13, 9, ...

2 How many squares are in the next diagram in the sequence?

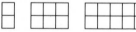

3 The *n*th term of a sequence is $2n + 5$. Find these terms in the sequence:
  a 1st term **b** 50th term **c** 100th term

TEST

Sequences & number patterns (2)

● Finding the *n*th term of a linear sequence

Here the <u>difference</u> between <u>consecutive terms</u> is the <u>same</u>.

➤ Q & A

Find the *n*th term of this sequence: 6, 10, 14, 18, ...

Answer

❶ The difference between terms is <u>4</u>.

❷ Write out the <u>4</u> times-table: 4, 8, 12, 16, ...

➤ Method

❶ Find the <u>difference</u> between the terms.

❷ Write out the <u>times-table</u> for the difference found in ❶.

❸ <u>Compare</u> the times-table to the original sequence.

❸ The original sequence is always <u>2 more</u> than the 4 times-table.

$$4 + 2, 8 + 2, 12 + 2, 16 + 2, ... \quad \text{IIII}\blacktriangleright \quad 6, 10, 14, 18, ...$$

This means that the *n*th term is <u>$4n + 2$</u>.

The $4n$ gives the 4 times-table for $n = 1, 2, 3$, and so on.

The +2 is needed because the sequence is 2 more than the 4 times-table.

● Quadratic sequences

If the difference between terms isn't constant, the sequence may be quadratic. This just means it's <u>related to</u> the sequence of square numbers: <u>1, 4, 9, 16, ...</u>

➤ Q & A

Find the *n*th term of:

a 2, 5, 10, 17, ...

b 2, 8, 18, 32, ...

➤ Method

❶ See what you would have to do to <u>each term</u> to get a <u>square number</u>.

❷ Do whatever you did to each term to n^2. You have found the <u>*n*th term</u>.

Answer

a These are the square numbers <u>+ 1</u>, so *n*th term = $n^2 + 1$

b These are <u>double</u> the square numbers, so *n*th term = $2n^2$

Tip: Always test your answer by calculating a few terms, e.g. in part **b** put in $n = 1, 2, 3, 4$ to get $2 \times 1^2 = \underline{2}$, $2 \times 2^2 = \underline{8}$, $2 \times 3^2 = \underline{18}$, $2 \times 4^2 = \underline{32}$. ✓

Find the *n*th term of each of these sequences.

a 7, 10, 13, 16, 19, ...   **b** 1, 5, 9, 13, 17, ...   **c** 4, 7, 12, 19, ...

TEST

Functions & mappings

A <u>function</u> (also called a <u>mapping</u>) changes an <u>input to an output</u>.

❶ Functions can be written in words, e.g.
'<u>multiply the input by 2 and then add 4 to get the output</u>'.

❷ Functions can be shown by <u>function machines</u>:

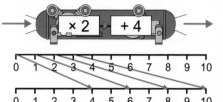

❸ Functions can be illustrated by <u>mapping diagrams</u>:

❹ Functions can be described using <u>algebra</u> (<u>letters</u>):

$x \longrightarrow 2x + 4$

● Inverse functions

An inverse function <u>reverses the direction</u> of a mapping. This can be shown in a mapping diagram.

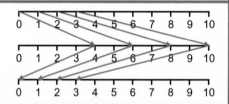

➤ Q & A

Find the inverse function of $x \rightarrow 2x + 4$.

Answer

Write the function as $y = 2x + 4$, then rearrange to get $x = ...$

$$y - 4 = 2x \qquad \text{[subtract 4 from both sides]}$$
$$(y - 4) \div 2 = x \qquad \text{[divide both sides by 2]}$$
$$x = \tfrac{1}{2}y - 2 \qquad \text{[swap sides and remove brackets]}$$

The final step is to write the function with x's only.

The inverse function is $x \rightarrow \tfrac{1}{2}x - 2$ (put inputs 4, 6, 8, 10 into this to see that it works)

---

1 a For this function machine, what is the output when the input is 4?

  b What is the input when the output is 12?
  c Write the function machine as a function using algebra.
2 a Find the inverse function of $x \rightarrow 10 - x$.
  b What do you notice about your answer to part **a**?

TEST

Speedy Revision

Coordinates

● Coordinates

Coordinates are pairs of numbers that give the <u>positions of points</u> on a graph.

$$(x, y)$$

The <u>first number</u> of the pair is called the <u>x-coordinate</u>; the <u>second number</u> is called the <u>y-coordinate</u>. (Notice they are in alphabetical order, i.e. x comes before y.)

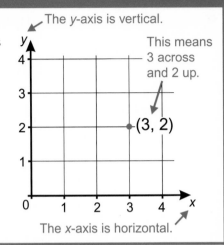

The y-axis is vertical.

This means 3 across and 2 up.

(3, 2)

The x-axis is horizontal.

● Negative coordinates

To plot points that have negative coordinates you need to extend the axes back past zero. This splits the graph into <u>4 different sections</u>.

A is at (2, 1)

B is at (–4, 1)

C is at (–2, –4)

D is at (3, –1)

> Remember: the first coordinate corresponds to the horizontal axis.

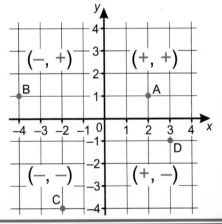

Write down the coordinates of the points on the graph on the right.

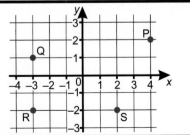

TEST

Straight-line graphs (1)

● Plotting and drawing straight-line graphs

The secret to drawing graphs is to first construct a <u>table of values</u>.

➤ Q & A

Complete this table of values for the equation $y = 2x + 2$ and then draw its graph.

x	−2	−1	0	1	2
$y = 2x + 2$		0		4	

Answer

The missing values are when $x = -2$, $x = 0$ and $x = 2$.
Putting these values into the equation gives:

when $x = -2$: $y = 2x + 2 = 2 \times (-2) + 2 = -4 + 2 = \underline{-2}$
when $x = 0$: $y = 2x + 2 = 2 \times 0 + 2 = 0 + 2 = \underline{2}$
when $x = 2$: $y = 2x + 2 = 2 \times 2 + 2 = 4 + 2 = \underline{6}$

So the completed table is:

x	−2	−1	0	1	2
$y = 2x + 2$	−2	0	2	4	6

Next plot the points one at a time on graph paper:

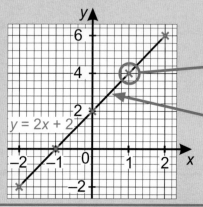

This pair of values gives the point (1, 4).

(1, 4) is plotted here.

Finally, use a <u>ruler</u> to draw a straight line through the points.

---

a Copy and complete the table of values for the equation: $y = 3x + 2$.

x	−2	−1	0	1	2
$y = 3x + 2$	−4			5	

b Draw the graph of $y = 3x + 2$ on graph paper.
(The x-axis should go from −2 to 2 and the y-axis should go from −4 to 8.)

TEST

◣ *Speedy* **Revision**

Straight-line graphs (2)

● Finding the gradient of a straight line

> ### Method
> ❶ Pick two points on the line.
> ❷ Draw a triangle through the points.
> ❸ Work out the height of the triangle and the width of the triangle.
> ❹ Use this formula to work out the gradient of the line:
>
> $$\text{Gradient} = \frac{\text{height}}{\text{width}}$$

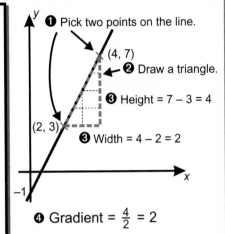

❶ Pick two points on the line.

(4, 7)

❷ Draw a triangle.

❸ Height = 7 – 3 = 4

(2, 3)

❸ Width = 4 – 2 = 2

❹ Gradient = $\frac{4}{2}$ = 2

● Positive or negative gradient?

If the graph slopes upwards (/) the gradient will be positive.
If the graph slopes downwards (\ ) the gradient will be negative.

● The general equation of a line is y = mx + c

All equations of straight lines can be written in the form y = mx + c.
m is the gradient. The greater the value of m the steeper the graph.
c is the y-intercept. This tells you the line cuts the y-axis at (0, c).

> ➤ The line above has gradient 2 and cuts the y-axis at y = –1.
> So the equation of the line is y = 2x – 1.

● Vertical and horizontal lines

x = a is the equation of a vertical line that cuts the x-axis at (a, 0).

y = b is the equation of a horizontal line that cuts the y-axis at (0, b).

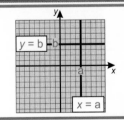

Write down the equation of the line that has gradient 5 and goes through the point (0, 4).

TEST

Real-life graphs

● Real-life straight-line graphs

The trick, again, is to first construct a <u>table of values</u>.

➤ Christina is taking part in a sponsored run. For every mile she runs she will raise £5 for her charity.

Miles run	Money raised
0	£0
1	£5
2	£10
3	£15
4	£20
5	£25

She raises £5 for 1 mile so she'll raise £5 × 5 = £25 for 5 miles.

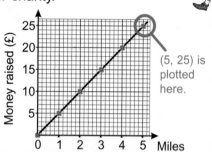

(5, 25) is plotted here.

● Distance–time graphs

In a <u>distance–time graph</u> the <u>gradient</u> gives the <u>velocity</u> (speed).

➤ Q & A

The graph shows Suki's walk to and from a local shop. Describe her journey in words.

Answer
❶ She starts <u>walking slowly</u>.
❷ She <u>stops</u> for a short while, perhaps because she bumps into a friend.
❸ She starts <u>walking more quickly</u>.
❹ She <u>stops</u> in the shop for a while.
❺ She <u>walks home without stopping</u>.

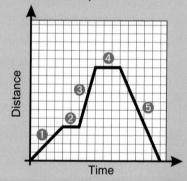

1 Describe the train journey shown in the graph.

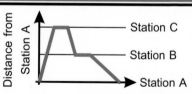

2 Calculate the gradient of the line in the sponsored run graph.

Inequalities

➤ Q & A

List all the integer values of n that satisfy $-2 \leqslant n < 3$.

Answer

$\underline{-2, -1, 0, 1, 2}$

Include –2 because the first sign means greater than or <u>equal to –2</u>.

Stop at 2 because the second sign means <u>less than 3</u>.

The four inequality symbols

< means '<u>less than</u>'.

⩽ means '<u>less than or equal to</u>'.

> means '<u>greater than</u>'.

⩾ means '<u>greater than or equal to</u>'.

● Solving an inequality

You solve inequalities in <u>exactly</u> the same way as equations, with one exception: if you <u>multiply or divide by a negative number</u> you must <u>reverse the inequality</u> symbol. This can be tricky, so <u>don't do it!</u> Follow the method below and you'll never have to.

➤ Q & A

Solve $4x + 1 > x - 5$.

Answer

$4x + 1 > x - 5$

$3x + 1 > -5$ $[-x]$

$3x > -6$ $[-1]$

$x > -2$ $[\div 3]$

➤ Method

❶ Get rid of the <u>smallest x-term</u>. This will give you a <u>positive</u> number of x on one side only.

❷ <u>Add/subtract</u> any <u>numbers</u> on the x side to/from both sides.

❸ <u>Divide both sides</u> by the number multiplying x.

● Showing inequalities on a number line

➤ Q & A

Show $x < -2$ and $0 \leqslant x < 5$ on a number line.

O means <u>not included</u>

● means <u>is included</u>

Use arrows to show more numbers are included.

Answer

<u>Shade</u> this circle because the inequality was '⩽', so <u>0 is included</u>.

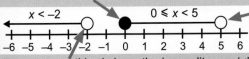

$x < -2$ $0 \leqslant x < 5$

<u>Do not shade</u> as the inequality was '<', so <u>5 is not included</u>.

<u>Do not shade</u> this circle as the inequality was '<', so <u>–2 is not included</u>.

See next page for TEST.

Speedy Revision

Trial & improvement

● Solving equations

Essential: you must show all your working.

➤ Q & A

The equation $x^3 + x = 75$ has a solution between 4 and 5. Use trial and improvement to find the solution to 2 d.p.

Answer

➤ Method

❶ Make a sensible guess for x and substitute it into the equation.

❷ If the left-hand side is too big/small, take a smaller/bigger guess.

❸ Stop when you have two numbers that bound x and round to the same number.

x	$x^3 + x$		
4.5	95.625	too big	x is between 4 and 4.5
4.2	78.288	too big	x is between 4 and 4.2
4.1	73.021	too small	x is between 4.1 and 4.2
4.15	75.623375	too big	x is between 4.1 and 4.15
4.13	74.574997	too small	x is between 4.13 and 4.15
4.14	75.097944	too big	x is between 4.13 and 4.14

To see if the solution is 4.13 or 4.14 you need to try the mid-value:

4.135	74.83616...	too small	x is between 4.135 and 4.14

4.135 & 4.14 both round to 4.14, so the solution is $x = 4.14$ to 2 d.p.

The last step in the **Q & A** can be seen clearly on a number line:

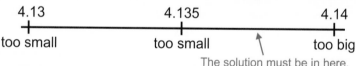

4.13   4.135   4.14

too small   too small   too big

The solution must be in here.

Use trial and improvement to find the solution of $x^3 - x = 50$ correct to 2 decimal places.

TEST

Inequalities (page 35)

1 **a** List integer values of n that satisfy $-5 < n \leqslant 1$.
   b Show the solution to $-5 < n \leqslant 1$ on a number line.
2 **a** Solve $2x + 2 < x + 4$.
   b Show the solution on a number line.

TEST

Units of measurement

● Metric units

Commonly used metric units of length are
millimetre (mm), centimetre (cm), metre (m),
kilometre (km); masses are gram (g), kilogram
(kg); capacities are millilitre (ml), litre (l).

Length
10 mm = 1 cm
100 cm = 1 m
1000 m = 1 km

Mass
1000 g = 1 kg

Capacity
1000 ml = 1 litre

● Converting between metric units

Metric units are based on the decimal system
and so it is easy to convert between them.

- To change from small units to large units divide.
- To change from large units to small units multiply.

➤ Examples

300 cm = 3 m (÷ 100)
7 litres = 7000 ml (× 1000)
5000 g = 5 kg (÷ 1000)
30 cm = 300 mm (× 10)

Divide because this is going from small to
large units. The 100 comes from the fact
that 100 cm = 1 m.

Multiply because this is going from large
to small units. The 10 comes from the fact
that 10 mm = 1 cm.

● Imperial units

Length
12 inches = 1 foot
3 feet = 1 yard

Mass
16 ounces = 1 pound

Capacity
8 pints = 1 gallon

Imperial units are getting
a bit old fashioned.

● Converting between metric and imperial units

Length
1 foot is roughly 30 cm
1 mile is roughly 1.6 km

Mass
1 pound is roughly 450 g
1 ounce is roughly 30 g

Capacity
1 pint is roughly 0.5 litre
1 gallon is roughly 4.5 litres

1 Convert these to centimetres: **a** 2 m **b** 60 mm

2 How many grams in: **a** an ounce **b** a pound?

TEST

Reading scales & accuracy

● Reading scales

You should always work out how much each division is worth.

> ### ➤ Examples

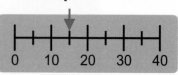

There are 2 spaces
between 10 and 20.
So each space is worth 5.
The reading shows 15.

There are 5
spaces
between 20
and 30.
So each space
is worth 2.
The reading
shows 26.

● Accuracy of measurement

Measurements are often given to the nearest whole unit.
The measurement could really be up to half a unit more or less than
the given value.

> ### ➤ Example

A length is given as 17 cm to the nearest centimetre.
This means that the actual length could be anywhere between
16.5 cm and 17.5 cm.

The actual measurement
could be anywhere in here.

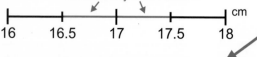

cm

'Less than' because
length cannot equal
17.5 as this would
have been rounded
to 18 cm.

As an inequality this is 16.5 ≤ length < 17.5.

---

1 Read these scales:

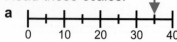

2 Write down the upper and lower limits for these:
  a 14 kg to the nearest kg   b 3 cm to the nearest mm

TEST

Estimating & measuring angles

● An angle is a measure of turn

$\frac{1}{4}$ turn = <u>90°</u> $\frac{1}{2}$ turn = <u>180°</u> $\frac{3}{4}$ turn = <u>270°</u>   Full turn = <u>360°</u>

➤ Q & A

Estimate the size of this angle:

Answer

You need to compare the angle to 90°, 180°, 270° and 360°.

The angle is more than 180° but less than 270°. A good estimate would be <u>210°</u>.

● Measuring angles with a protractor

Before measuring you must <u>estimate</u> the size of the angle.

This angle is acute. It looks about 45° (half a right angle).

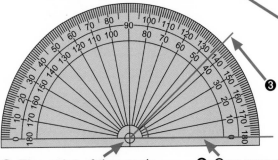

❸ Read the angle from the correct scale. The estimate was 45° so it must be <u>44°</u> (not 136°).

❶ The point of the angle should be at the cross.

❷ One arm of the angle should be along the 0° line.

---

1   Estimate the size of these angles.   **a**   **b**

2   Measure the angles in **Q1** with a protractor.

TEST

Angles & parallel lines

● Angle facts

An <u>acute angle</u> is less than 90°.

A <u>right angle</u> is 90°.

An <u>obtuse angle</u> is between 90° and 180°.

A <u>reflex angle</u> is more than 180°.

Angles on a straight line add up to 180°.

$$a + b = 180°$$

Angles at a point add up to 360°.

$$c + d + e + f = 360°$$

Vertically opposite angles are equal.

$$p = r \text{ and } q = s$$

● Parallel lines

Alternate angles are equal.

$$u = v$$

(The angles are in a Z-shape.)

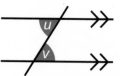

Corresponding angles are equal.

$$w = x$$

(The angles are in an F-shape.)

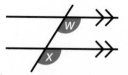

Work out the size of the lettered angles.

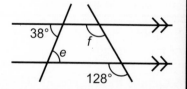

TEST

Polygons

● The angles in a triangle add up to 180°

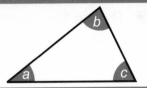

$$a + b + c = 180°$$

● The angles in a quadrilateral add up to 360°

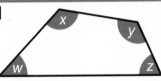

$$w + x + y + z = 360°$$

● Interior and exterior angles

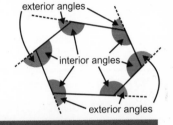

The angles <u>inside</u> a polygon are called <u>interior angles</u>.

<u>Exterior angles</u> are found on the <u>outside</u> when the <u>sides are extended</u>.

<u>Learn</u> these two formulae:

❶ Sum of exterior angles = 360°

❷ Sum of interior angles = (number of sides – 2) × 180°

● Regular polygons

The <u>sides and angles</u> of a <u>regular polygon</u> are all the <u>same size</u>.

➤ Q & A

What is the size of an interior angle in a regular pentagon?

Answer

Using formula **❷** above we get:

Sum of interior angles of a regular pentagon = (5 – 2) × 180° = 540°

There are 5 equal interior angles, so size of one = 540° ÷ 5 = <u>108°</u>

---

1 Two interior angles of a triangle are 57° and 74°. What size is the other angle?

2 What size are the interior and exterior angles of
a a square **b** a regular hexagon?

TEST

Symmetry & properties of shapes (1)

● Reflection symmetry

If a shape can be folded so that one
half fits exactly on the other, it is
said to have reflection symmetry
(also known as line symmetry).

Fold line (also called mirror line)

Some shapes have more than one line of symmetry; some don't
have any:

Square | Equilateral triangle | No lines of symmetry
4 lines of symmetry | 3 lines of symmetry

● Rotation symmetry

A shape has rotation symmetry if it looks exactly the same when
turned. The order of rotation symmetry is the number of times a
shape fits exactly over itself during a full-turn about its centre.

➤ Q & A

What is the order of
rotation symmetry
of these shapes?

Order 4   Order 3   Order 1

Note: Order of rotation symmetry 1 means no rotation symmetry.

● Plane symmetry

This is basically reflection symmetry in 3-D shapes.
A plane of symmetry cuts a solid shape in half so that one half is the
mirror image of the other.

➤ Q & A

Draw a cube and an isosceles triangular prism.
Indicate one plane of symmetry in each.

Answer

Both of these shapes have
more than one plane of
symmetry. See TEST Q2.

Symmetry & properties of shapes (2)

● Four types of triangle

Right-angled
One 90° angle

Isosceles
2 equal sides
2 equal angles
1 line of symmetry

Equilateral
3 equal sides
3 equal angles
3 lines of symmetry
Rotation symmetry of order 3

Scalene
All sides and angles
are different

● Quadrilaterals (shapes with 4 sides)

Square
4 lines of symmetry
Rotation symmetry
of order 4
All angles are 90°
All sides equal
2 pairs of parallel sides

Rhombus
2 lines of symmetry
Rotation symmetry
of order 2
All sides equal
Opposite angles equal
2 pairs of parallel sides

Rectangle
2 lines of symmetry
Rotation symmetry
of order 2
All angles are 90°
Opposite sides equal
2 pairs of parallel sides

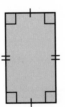

Kite
1 line of symmetry
No rotation symmetry
2 pairs of adjacent sides
equal
1 pair of opposite sides equal

Parallelogram
No lines of symmetry
Rotation symmetry
of order 2
Opposite sides
equal and parallel
Opposite angles equal

Trapezium
No lines of symmetry
(unless isosceles)
No rotation symmetry
One pair of parallel sides

Parallel lines never meet.
Perpendicular lines cross at right angles.

---

1 For each shape write down the: **i** number of lines of symmetry
ii order of rotation symmetry.

a   **b** 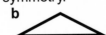 **c**

2 Draw a different plane of symmetry on the cube and
isosceles triangular prism on the previous page.

TEST

Speedy Revision

Reflection

● Reflecting a shape in a mirror line

When you reflect a shape in a mirror line its size and shape are <u>not</u> changed. The original shape is called the <u>object</u> and its reflection is called the <u>image</u>.

➤ Q & A

Reflect the shape in the mirror line.

Answer

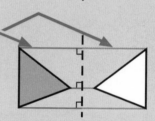

❶ Draw a line from each corner <u>at right angles</u> to the mirror line.
❷ Extend the lines exactly the same distance on the other side of the mirror line.
❸ Join up the ends of the lines to show the image.

● Two mirror lines

You can make a symmetrical pattern by reflecting in two mirror lines.

Keep reflecting until the pattern is complete.

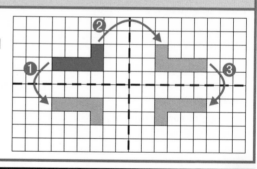

Copy and then reflect these shapes in the mirror lines:

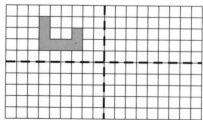

a

b

TEST

44

Rotation

● Turning shapes

A rotation turns a shape through an angle about some fixed point.
A rotation can be in a <u>clockwise</u> or <u>anticlockwise</u> direction.

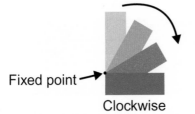

Fixed point →

Clockwise   Anticlockwise

➤ Q & A

Rotate the shape 90° <u>clockwise</u>
about the corner marked with a dot.

Answer

❶ Draw around the shape on
 tracing paper.

❷ Pin the tracing paper down with
 your pencil at the dot.

❸ Rotate the tracing paper 90°
 clockwise.

❹ Draw over the traced shape
 (press down quite hard) so that
 you can see where to draw the
 rotated shape.

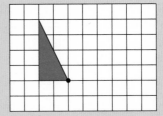

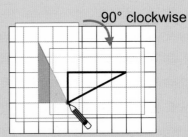

90° clockwise

Rotate these shapes 90° <u>anticlockwise</u> about the dots:

a

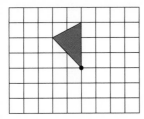

b

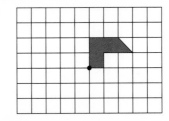

TEST

Translation

● Sliding shapes

A translation is where you slide a shape along <u>without</u> rotating or reflecting it.

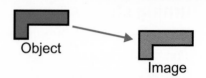

Object

Image

A translation moves a shape:
❶ a specific distance <u>left or right</u>
❷ and then a specific distance <u>up or down</u>.

➤ Q & A

Translate the triangle 5 squares to the right and 3 squares up.

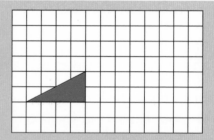

Answer

❶ Put your pencil on a corner of the shape.
❷ Move your pencil 5 squares right and 3 squares up.
❸ Draw the shape in the new position.

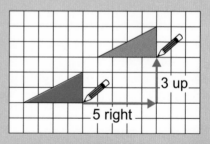

3 up

5 right

---

1 Translate the shape 4 units to the right and 2 units up.

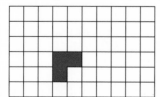

2 Translate the shape 5 units to the left and 2 units down.

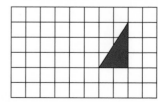

TEST

46

Enlargement

An <u>enlargement</u> changes the <u>size</u> of an object, but not its shape. To describe an enlargement you give its <u>centre</u> and <u>scale factor</u>.

➤ **Q & A**

a Enlarge A by a scale factor of 2 about (–1, 1). Label the image B.

b D is an enlargement of C. Describe the enlargement.

Answer

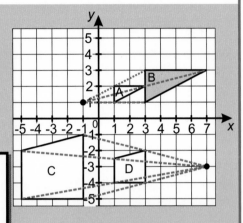

a

➤ **Method for a**

❶ <u>Draw 'rays'</u> from the centre of enlargement through the vertices of A.

❷ Draw the vertices of B on these rays, <u>twice as far</u> from the centre.

Twice as far, because the scale factor is 2.

b Enlargement with scale factor $\frac{1}{2}$, centre (7, –3)

The scale factor is a fraction because the image is smaller than the object.

➤ **Method for b**

❶ <u>Draw 'rays'</u> through corresponding vertices. The point where these cross is the <u>centre</u>.

❷ Measure <u>corresponding lengths</u> to find the scale factor.

1 Draw axes with both x and y from –10 to 10.

  a Plot these points. Join them in order. Label the shape A.
    (–5, –1), (–7, –5), (–5, –3), (–1, –5), (–5, –1)

  b Enlarge A using:
    i centre (–7, –9), s.f. 2   **ii** centre (–7, –9), s.f. $\frac{1}{2}$

2 Look again at the **Q & A**.
  Describe the transformation from **a** B to A **b** D to C.

TEST

Perimeter & circumference

● Perimeter

Perimeter is the distance around the outside edge of a 2-D shape.
It is measured in mm, cm, m or km.

➤ Q & A

What is the perimeter of this shape?

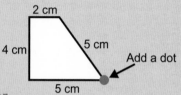

Add a dot

Answer

Start at the dot and add the sides up
clockwise: 5 + 4 + 2 + 5 = 16 cm

➤ Method

❶ Mark a corner with a dot.

❷ Start at the dot, add the sides as you go around the shape. Stop when you get back to the dot.

❸ Essential: Show your working.

● Circumference of a circle

The circumference is the perimeter of a circle.

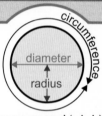

Circumference = π × diameter (C = πd)

π ≈ 3.14 or 3.142 or press **π** (π is a Greek letter, pronounced 'pie'.)

➤ Q & A

This circle has a radius of 5 cm. What is its circumference?

5 cm

Answer

The radius is 5 cm, so the
diameter = 5 cm × 2 = 10 cm.

Circumference = π × diameter = 3.14 × 10 = 31.4 cm

➤ Method

❶ Find the diameter (the diameter is twice the radius).

❷ Use the formula: C = πd

---

1 Work out the perimeters of these shapes:

a

4 cm

10 cm

b

2 cm

2 cm

4 cm

10 cm

TEST

2 What is the circumference of a circle with radius 8 cm?

48

Areas of triangles & quadrilaterals

● Area of a triangle

Area = $\frac{1}{2}$ × base × height

$A = \frac{1}{2} \times b \times h$

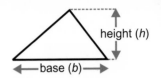

● Area of a rectangle

Area = length × width

$A = l \times w$

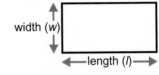

● Area of a parallelogram

Area = base × perpendicular height

$A = b \times h$

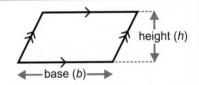

● Area of a trapezium

Area = $\frac{1}{2}$ × sum of parallel sides × height between them

$A = \frac{1}{2} \times (a + b) \times h$

Essential: for triangles, parallelograms and trapeziums make sure that you use the height that's at right angles to the base.

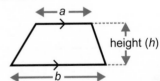

Memorise the formulae above (get someone to test you), then work out the areas of these shapes (remember your units):

a

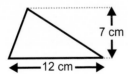

b

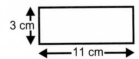

c

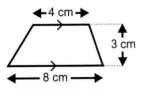

d

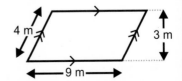

TEST

Areas of circles & composite shapes

● Area of a circle

Area = π × radius squared

$$A = \pi r^2$$

Use the **π** button (or π ≈ 3.14 or 3.142).

● Area of composite shapes

➤ Q & A

Work out the area of this shape:

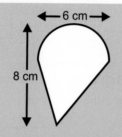

Answer

❶ The shape is a <u>semicircle</u> on top of a <u>triangle</u>.

❷ First, find the area of the semicircle:

Diameter is 6 cm, so the <u>radius is 3 cm</u>.

The <u>area of a circle</u> with radius 3 cm is π × 3² = 3.14 × 9 = 28.26 cm².

So the <u>area of the semicircle</u> is $\frac{1}{2}$ × 28.26 = <u>14.13 cm²</u>.

Next, work out the area of the triangle:

The height of the triangle is 8 – 3 = 5 cm. The base is 6 cm.

So the <u>area of the triangle</u> is $\frac{1}{2}$ × 5 × 6 = <u>15 cm²</u>.

❸ Total area of the shape = 14.13 cm² + 15 cm² = <u>29.13 cm²</u>

➤ Method

❶ Split the shape into <u>simple shapes</u>.

❷ <u>Work out the area</u> of each simple shape.

❸ <u>Add</u> up the areas of the simple shapes to get the <u>total area</u> of the big shape.

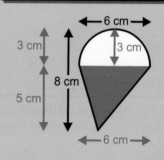

Work out the areas of these shapes:

a

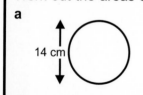

14 cm

b

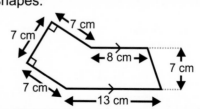

TEST

More circles

● Arcs & sectors

Learn these formulae for calculating the length of an arc and the area of a sector.

$$\text{Arc length} = \frac{\theta}{360} \times 2\pi r$$

$$\text{Sector area} = \frac{\theta}{360} \times \pi r^2$$

arc · sector

> ### ➤ Example

Arc length $= \frac{90°}{360°} \times 2\pi r$

$= 0.25 \times 2 \times \pi \times 5 = \underline{7.85 \text{ cm}}$

5 cm

Sector area $= \frac{90°}{360°} \times \pi r^2$

$= 0.25 \times \pi \times 5^2 = \underline{19.6 \text{ cm}^2}$

Note: This is the <u>minor sector</u> (i.e. the small bit). The big bit is the <u>major sector</u>.

● Circle theorems

Make sure you know these <u>two facts</u> about circles.

❶ The <u>tangent</u> at any point on a circle is <u>perpendicular</u> to the <u>radius</u> at that point.

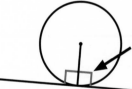

tangent and radius are at right angles (90°)

❷ A line drawn from the <u>centre</u> of a circle <u>perpendicular</u> to a chord <u>bisects the chord</u>.

AB = BC

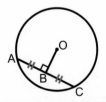

The circle has a radius of 3 cm.
a Calculate the length of the grey arc.
b Calculate the area of the grey sector.

120°

TEST

Pythagoras' theorem (1)

● **The square of the hypotenuse is equal to the sum of the squares of the other two sides**

Using letters this is written as:

$$h^2 = a^2 + b^2$$

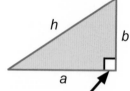

h is the hypotenuse, which is always the longest side (the side opposite the right angle).

Pythagoras' theorem only works in right-angled triangles.

● Finding h given a and b

➤ **Q & A**

What is the length of the hypotenuse?

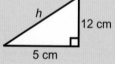

12 cm
5 cm

Answer

From the diagram: $a = 5$, $b = 12$.

$h^2 = 5^2 + 12^2$

∴ $h^2 = 25 + 144 = 169$

∴ $h = \sqrt{169}$

∴ $h = 13$

So the length of the hypotenuse is 13 cm.

➤ **Method**

❶ Write down the values of a and b.

❷ Put these values into $h^2 = a^2 + b^2$.

❸ Find h by solving the equation (take the square root of both sides).

(∴ means 'therefore'.)

● Finding b given h and a

➤ **Q & A**

Find the missing length.

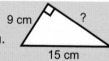

9 cm   ?
15 cm

Answer

From the diagram: $h = 15$, $a = 9$.

$15^2 = 9^2 + b^2$

∴ $225 = 81 + b^2$

∴ $b^2 = 225 - 81 = 144$

∴ $b = \sqrt{144}$

∴ $b = 12$, so missing length is 12 cm.

➤ **Method**

❶ Write down the values of h and a (a is always the given side that isn't the hypotenuse).

❷ Put these values into $h^2 = a^2 + b^2$.

❸ Find b by solving the equation.

Pythagoras' theorem (2)

● Finding the distance between two points

➤ Q & A

Work out the distance between the points P(2, 1) and Q(5, 3).

Answer

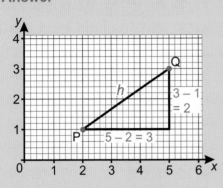

➤ Method

❶ Sketch the two points with a right-angled triangle drawn through them.

❷ Work out the lengths of the horizontal and vertical sides of the triangle (these are your a and b).

❸ Use $h^2 = a^2 + b^2$ to work out the hypotenuse (this is the distance between the two points).

From the diagram: $a = 3, b = 2$.

$h^2 = 3^2 + 2^2$ [put values into $h^2 = a^2 + b^2$]

$\therefore h^2 = 9 + 4 = 13$

$\therefore h = \sqrt{13}$

$\therefore h = 3.6$ (to 1 d.p.)

So distance between P and Q is 3.6 units.

(You can use the √ button on your calculator to work out square roots.)

---

1 Use Pythagoras' theorem to work out the missing lengths. Give your answers to 1 d.p.

a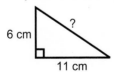

b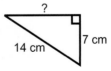

c

2 Work out the distance between these points:
   a (4, 5) and (11, 13)   **b** (24, 11) and (12, –4)

3 Work out the coordinates of the midpoints of the lines between the points in **Q2**.
   (Hint: add the x-coordinates then divide by 2, do the same for the y-coordinates.)

TEST

Nets & 3-D shapes; plans & elevations

● Nets

A <u>net</u> is a 3-D shape folded out <u>flat</u>.
Below are some 3-D shapes, with
their nets, that you need to know.

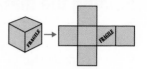

Cube

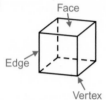

Face
Edge
Vertex

There are 11 different nets for a cube.
Here are two, can you draw the others? (See p76)

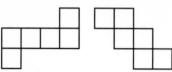

Cuboid

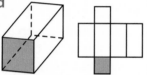

Square-based pyramid

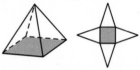

Triangular prism

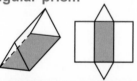

Regular tetrahedron

● Plans & elevations

A <u>plan</u> of a 3-D shape is what you see if you look down from <u>above</u>.
An <u>elevation</u> is what you see if you look from the <u>front or side</u>.

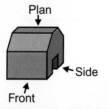

Plan
←Side
Front

Plan   Front   Side

1 How many faces, edges and vertices do these have?
   a cuboid **b** triangular prism
2 Draw plan, front and side elevations for a triangular prism.

TEST

Volume & surface area (1)

● Volume

The volume of a 3-D solid is the amount of space it takes up.
It is measured in mm^3, cm^3, m^3 or km^3. ◄—— Notice the 'cubed' bit.

If the shape is made from cubes you can find the volume by counting the cubes. If not you'll have to use a formula:

● Volume of a cuboid

Volume = length × width × height

$V = l \times w \times h$

(This formula also works for a cube, i.e. $V = l \times l \times l = l^3$.)

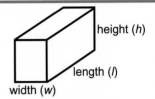

height (h)
length (l)
width (w)

● Volume of a prism

Volume = area of cross-section × length

$V = A \times l$

(A prism is a shape with the same cross-section all along its length.)

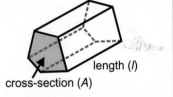

length (l)
cross-section (A)

➤ Q & A

Work out the volume of this triangular prism:

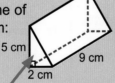

5 cm
9 cm
2 cm

Answer

The area of the cross-section (triangular end) is
$\frac{1}{2} \times 2 \times 5 = 5$ cm².

The length is 9 cm.
So volume = $A \times l = 5 \times 9 = \underline{45\ cm^3}$.

➤ Method

❶ Work out the area of the cross-section.
❷ Write down the length of the prism.
❸ Use the formula
$V = A \times l$
to work out the volume.
❹ Remember your units
(usually cm^3 or m^3).

● Volume of a cylinder

A cylinder is a prism with circular cross-section.

$V = \pi r^2 \times h$

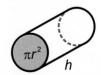

πr^2
h

Volume & surface area (2)

● Surface area

The <u>surface area</u> of a 3-D shape is the <u>total area</u> of all its <u>faces</u>.

➤ Q & A

Work out the surface area of this cuboid.

3 cm   4 cm

2 cm

Answer

First sketch the net of the cuboid.

The task now is to work out the area of each of the six rectangles (faces).

Two have an area of 2 cm × 3 cm = 6 cm²
Two have an area of 2 cm × 4 cm = 8 cm²
Two have an area of 3 cm × 4 cm = 12 cm²

So the total surface area is
6 + 6 + 8 + 8 + 12 + 12 = <u>52 cm²</u>.

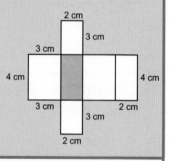

● Changing units

➤ Q & A

The volume of a cupboard is 4.5 m³. What is the volume in cm³?

Answer

4.5 m³

= 4.5 (100 cm)³   [1 m = 100 cm]

= 4.5 × 100³ cm³

= 4.5 × 1 000 000 cm³

= <u>4 500 000 cm³</u>

➤ Method

❶ Write the area/volume down.

❷ Write it again with the <u>new length unit</u> in place of the <u>old length unit</u>.

❸ <u>Square</u> (for area) or <u>cube</u> (for volume) the new length unit.

❹ Multiply the numbers.

To go from cm³ to m³, divide by 100³.

---

1 Work out the volume & surface area of each of these shapes:

a 13 m   12 m   20 m   5 m

b 5 m   6 m   4.2 m

c 20 cm   6 cm

TEST

2 Change the units in your answer in **1a** to cm³ and cm² & **1c** to m³ and m².

Speedy Revision

Bearings & scale drawings

● Bearings

❶ A bearing is <u>an angle</u> that gives a <u>direction</u>.
❷ Bearings are measured <u>clockwise</u> from the <u>North line</u>.
❸ All bearings are given as <u>3 figures</u>.

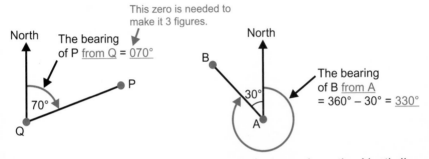

This zero is needed to make it 3 figures.

North
The bearing of P <u>from Q</u> = <u>070°</u>
70°
Q
P

North
B
30°
A
The bearing of B <u>from A</u> = 360° − 30° = <u>330°</u>

Look out for the word <u>from</u>; it tells you where to draw the North line and measure <u>from</u>.

● Scale drawings & maps

Scale drawings usually have a scale something like '<u>1 cm = 5 m</u>'. This means that a length of <u>1 cm on the drawing</u> represents a distance of <u>5 m in real life</u>. A scale can also be given as a <u>ratio</u>, e.g. 1 cm = 5 m can be written as <u>1 : 500</u>.

➤ Example

The map shows the positions of three towns.

The distance between Berlham and Carwick is <u>3 cm</u> on the map.

The scale is <u>1 cm = 20 km</u>, so this means that the distance in real life is <u>20 km × 3 = 60 km</u>.

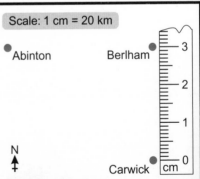

Scale: 1 cm = 20 km

● Abinton   Berlham ●

N

Carwick ●

---

1 In the example above, what is the bearing of:
  a Berlham from Abinton   **b** Abinton from Berlham?
2 What is the distance in real life between Abinton and Carwick?

TEST

Speedy Revision

Compound measures

● **Speed** = $\dfrac{\textbf{Distance}}{\textbf{Time}}$

There are 3 ways of writing this formula:

$S = \dfrac{D}{T}$ $T = \dfrac{D}{S}$ $D = S \times T$

All 3 ways can be remembered using this '<u>formula triangle</u>':

➤ Q & A

A car travels at 70 mph for 2.5 hours. How far does it go?

Answer

<u>Distance</u> is needed so cover up D.

This gives D = S × T

D = 70 × 2.5 = 175

The car travels <u>175 miles</u>.

➤ Method

❶ <u>Cover up what you want</u> on the <u>formula triangle</u>. Write down the formula this gives.

❷ Write the formula with the <u>numbers you know</u>. (Make sure the units <u>match</u>. e.g. if the speed has <u>hours</u> in it, the time must be in <u>hours</u>.)

❸ Calculate the answer.

● **Density** = $\dfrac{\textbf{Mass}}{\textbf{Volume}}$

Like the one for speed, this formula can also be written in a '<u>formula triangle</u>': ➤

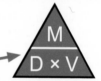

➤ Q & A

A block has a density of 22 kg/m³. The mass of the block is 88 kg. What is the volume of the block?

Answer

<u>Volume</u> is needed so cover up V.

This gives $V = \dfrac{M}{D}$

So $V = \dfrac{88}{22} = 4$

The block has a volume of <u>4 m³</u>.

---

1 How long will a car travelling at 60 km/h take to travel 40 km?

2 Calculate the mass of 2 m³ of wood of density 500 kg/m³.

TEST

Speedy Revision

Constructions & loci (1)

● How to construct an equilateral triangle

❶
Draw a line of the
length you want the
sides to be, e.g. 5 cm.

❷
Set your compasses to 5 cm.
Draw two crossing arcs from
the ends of the line.

❸
Join the point where
the arcs crossed to
the ends of the line.

You've also
constructed
an angle of 60°.

● Perpendicular bisector of a line

Perpendicular means 'at right angles'.
Bisect means 'cut in half'.

This is similar to
constructing an
equilateral triangle.

You just have to draw
two more crossing
arcs on the other side
of the line.

Set your compasses
to more than half the
length of the line.

You've also
found the
midpoint of
the line.

● Perpendicular from a point to a line

❶ Draw two arcs on the line, centred
on the point. Keep your compasses
set at the same distance.

❷ Draw two crossing arcs on the other
side of the line, with the compasses
centred on the arcs on the line.

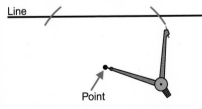

Line

Point

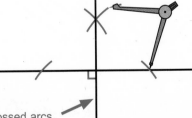

❸ Draw a line from the point to the crossed arcs.
This is the perpendicular from the point to the line.

---

1 Construct an equilateral triangle of side 6 cm.
2 Draw a line 8 cm long. Construct its perpendicular bisector.
3 Construct the perpendicular from a point to a line.

TEST

Constructions & loci (2)

● Perpendicular from a point on a line

❶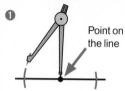

Point on the line

❷

❸

Draw arcs on the line either side of the point. Use the same radius.

Increase the radius. Draw two crossing arcs centred on the arcs on the line.

Join the original point to where the arcs crossed. This is the perpendicular.

● Bisector of an angle

❶

❷

❸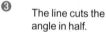

The line cuts the angle in half.

Draw two arcs on the arms of the angle, centred on the vertex.

Draw two crossing arcs inside the angle, centred on the arcs on the arms.

Join the vertex to the point where the arcs crossed.

● Loci

A locus is a set of points (often lines) that satisfy a given rule. Here are four loci that you should know (loci are in colour):

❶

❷

❸

❹

A fixed distance from a point is a circle.

A fixed distance from a straight line is two parallel straight lines.

Types ❶ & ❷ are often combined:

Fixed distance from a line segment

Equidistant from two points is the perpendular bisector of the line joining the two points.

Equidistant from two straight lines is the bisectors of the angles between the lines.

---

1 Construct a perpendicular 5 cm from the end of a 14 cm line.
2 Draw a 68° angle with a protractor. Bisect it with compasses.
3 Construct the locus of points 4 cm from a line 6 cm long.

TEST

Mean, median, mode, range (1)

You need to learn these.

$$\text{Mean} = \frac{\text{total of the values}}{\text{number of values}}$$

Median = the middle value when the numbers are put in order of size

Mode = the most common value

Range = highest value – lowest value

When people talk about 'the average' they're usually referring to 'the mean'. But be careful, because the median and mode are also 'averages'.

➤ Q & A

Find the mean, median, mode and range of this set of data:

5, 2, 3, 1, 5, 5, 10, 2, 3

Answer

Mean
The total of the values = 5 + 2 + 3 + 1 + 5 + 5 + 10 + 2 + 3 = 36
The number of values = 9 (count the numbers in the list)
So the mean = 36 ÷ 9 = 4.

Median
Rearrange the numbers in order of size.
1, 2, 2, 3, 3, 5, 5, 5,10
The middle number is 3, so the median = 3.

Mode
The most common value is 5 (there are three of them). So the mode = 5.

> If there are an even number of values, the median is halfway between the middle two.
> e.g. the median of
> 2, 3, 4, 5 is
> (3 + 4) ÷ 2 = 3.5.

Range
The highest value = 10 and the lowest value = 1.
So the range = 10 – 1 = 9.

Find the mode, median, mean and range of this set of data:
5, 6, 7, 4, 4, 12, 4

TEST

Mean, median, mode, range (2)

● Using the appropriate average

- ● The <u>mean</u> is useful as it takes all the values into account, but it can be distorted by extreme values, e.g. you wouldn't use the mean for this data: 1, 2, 2, 3, 5, 909.
- ● The <u>median</u> is useful when there are extreme values (as in the above example).
- ● The <u>mode</u> is useful when you just want the most common value, e.g. the week's best selling DVD.

● Comparing sets of data

When comparing two sets of data you should use one of the '<u>averages</u>' <u>and</u> the <u>range</u>.

➤ Q & A

Jane scored a mean of 2.9 goals per game last season and had a range of $4 - 2 = 2$. David scored a mean of 3.1 goals per game and had a range of $5 - 0 = 5$. Which player would you pick for the team?

Answer

Although David's mean score is higher, Jane's lower range shows that she scores more consistently. So you would probably want to pick Jane, but you could pick David if you wanted a riskier strategy.

Discrete & continuous data

● Discrete data

<u>Discrete data</u> can only take <u>certain values</u> and is often found by counting.
For example, the number of candles on a cake.

● Continuous data

<u>Continuous data</u> can take <u>any value</u> in a given range and is often found by measuring.
For example, the mass of rubbish in a bin.

Are these discrete or continuous data?
a The heights of students   **b** The number of people on a bus

TEST

Speedy Revision

Collecting data & two-way tables

● Collecting data

Two ways of collecting data are by:

❶ Observation: e.g. noting the colour of cars in a car park. Here you need to use a data collection sheet. This will often look like a simple tally/frequency chart (see page 64).

> Primary data is data you collect yourself.
> Secondary data is data that other people have collected.

❷ Questionnaire: Here you ask people suitable questions, e.g. 'What colour car do you drive?'

- ● Don't ask for information that is not needed, e.g. don't ask for a person's age if your survey doesn't need it.
- ● Make sure your question isn't leading (biased), e.g. never start a question 'Do you agree that ... ?'
- ● Allow for all possible answers. Using tick boxes is a good idea.

How many times have you been on an aeroplane?
Never ☐   1 to 2 ☐   3 to 4 ☐   5 & over ☐

● Two-way tables

Two-way tables show two sets of information in the one table.

> ➤ **Example** This two-way table shows the number of DVDs and CDs owned by a group of friends.

	DVDs	CDs	Total
Boys own	2	9	11
Girls own	18	31	49
Total	20	40	60

Boys own 9 CDs

Girls own 18 DVDs

There is a total of 60 DVDs and CDs

---

1   What is wrong with this survey question?
    How many dogs do you own?   None ☐   2 or more ☐

2   Complete this two-way table that shows the colours of pens owned by a group of friends.

	Black	Red	Blue	Total
Boys own	14		11	26
Girls own	7	7		34
Total	21	8	31	60

TEST

Frequency tables (1)

● Frequency tables

Frequency tables display data that has been counted.

➤ Q & A

Here are the favourite colours of 20 people.

red, red, blue, green, blue, green, blue, blue, red, green, red, red, blue, green, blue, red, green, blue, red, red

Show the data in a frequency table.

Answer

Use a tally column to help you count.

Colour	Tally	Frequency
Red	ⅢⅠ Ⅲ	8
Blue	ⅢⅠ ⅠⅠ	7
Green	ⅢⅠ	5
	Total	20

Write the tallies as numbers in the frequency column.

Total the numbers in the frequency column.
This helps make sure you haven't made a mistake.
The question said 20 people so this is correct.

➤ Tallies

Always use tallies when you are counting items of data. You should group your tallies in fives.

● Grouping data

If you are given a long list of numbers, you can group the numbers into intervals such as $20 \leqslant n < 30$.

For example, this list:

22, 14, 15, 23, 33, 14, 37, 36, 22, 25, 31, 6, 13, 8, 23, 23, 30, 20

is shown in the frequency table.

Number, n	Tally	Frequency
$0 \leqslant n < 10$	ⅠⅠ	2
$10 \leqslant n < 20$	ⅠⅠⅠⅠ	4
$20 \leqslant n < 30$	ⅢⅠ ⅠⅠ	7
$30 \leqslant n < 40$	ⅢⅠ	5
	Total	18

Note: 20 belongs to $20 \leqslant n < 30$, not $10 \leqslant n < 20$.

Show this data in a frequency table (group as in the example above): 20, 12, 3, 45, 32, 9, 12, 5, 23, 25, 32, 31, 40, 32, 12, 33

TEST

Speedy Revision

Frequency tables (2)

● Estimating the mean from grouped data

You don't have the raw data, so you can only <u>estimate</u> the mean.

> ### ➤ Q & A

The table shows the lengths of candles on a birthday cake.

Estimate the mean length.

Answer

> ### ➤ Method
> ❶ Add a <u>column of midpoints</u>.
> ❷ <u>Multiply</u> each <u>midpoint</u> by its <u>frequency</u>.
> ❸ <u>Total</u> this column.
> ❹ <u>Divide</u> by the <u>total frequency</u>.

Length (L mm)	Frequency	Midpoint	Freq. × midpoint
$80 \leqslant L < 90$	2	85	170
$90 \leqslant L < 100$	2	95	190
$100 \leqslant L < 110$	3	105	315
$110 \leqslant L < 120$	6	115	690
$120 \leqslant L < 130$	3	125	375
Total	16	Total	1740

Estimated mean = 1740 ÷ 16 = <u>109 mm</u> (to nearest mm)

● Median

You can't give an exact value for the <u>median</u>, but you can say which <u>group it's in</u>.

> ➤ The median is the 8.5th value, which is in the $110 \leqslant L < 120$ group.

● Modal group

The <u>modal group</u> has the <u>highest frequency</u>.

> ➤ The modal group is $110 \leqslant L < 120$.

These are the heights (h cm) of 20 students:
152, 167, 169, 158, 177, 165, 172, 168, 156, 161,
163, 166, 171, 157, 162, 169, 168, 155, 176, 167

a Put the data into a frequency table with groups
$150 \leqslant h < 155$, $155 \leqslant h < 160$, ... (Use tallies to help you.)
b Use the table to calculate an estimate for the mean.
c Which group is the median in? **d** Which is the modal group?

TEST

Bar charts & frequency diagrams

● Bar charts

In a bar chart the <u>frequencies</u> from your frequency table are represented by the <u>heights of the bars</u>.

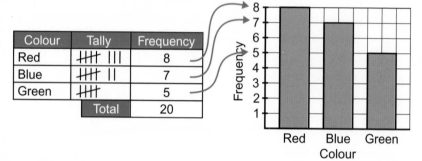

Colour	Tally	Frequency
Red	⊞ |||	8
Blue	⊞ ||	7
Green	⊞	5
Total		20

<u>Bar charts</u> are used to show discrete data. The bars <u>do not touch</u>.

● Frequency diagrams

Frequency diagrams show <u>grouped continuous data</u>.

The bars <u>touch</u>.

The diagram shows the data from the **Q & A** on page 65.

Make sure the bars have <u>equal widths</u>.

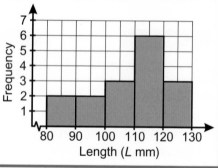

● Frequency polygons

A frequency polygon is a line graph of <u>frequency against midpoint of the groups</u>.

Joining the tops of the frequency diagram bars is the <u>easiest way</u> to draw a frequency polygon.

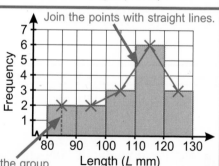

For the height data in the TEST on page 65, draw:
a a frequency diagram **b** a frequency polygon.

TEST

Stem & leaf diagrams; line graphs

● Stem & leaf diagrams

These are like <u>bar charts</u>, but each bar displays the <u>actual data</u>.

▶ Q & A

Show this data on a stem and leaf diagram.

4, 5, 8, 12, 18, 19, 20, 22, 24, 25, 25, 26, 31, 32, 34, 36, 40, 43, 44

Answer

The 'stem' is the first part of the number, in this case Tens.

The 'leaf' is the rest of the number, in this case Units.

0	4 5 8
1	2 8 9
2	0 2 4 5 5 6
3	1 2 4 6
4	0 3 4

The <u>leaves</u> should be given in <u>order of size</u>. If the original list of data had been jumbled you would have had to re-order the leaves.

Always include a key. → Key: 1 | 8 means 18

● Line graphs

A line graph is a set of <u>points joined with straight lines</u>.

This type of graph is very good for showing <u>trends</u> over periods of <u>time</u> (they are sometimes called 'time series').

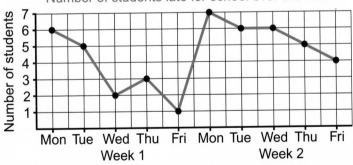

Number of students late for school over two weeks

1 30 students got these marks in a test:
50, 75, 51, 68, 72, 48, 62, 58, 65, 62, 42, 70, 54, 67, 60,
73, 74, 69, 62, 59, 63, 72, 62, 63, 57, 69, 49, 56, 58, 70
Draw a stem and leaf diagram to show the data.

2 Describe any trends you can see in the line graph above.

Pie charts

● Drawing pie charts

➤ Q & A (1)

Draw a pie chart for this shopping budget.

Food	£31
Drinks	£12
Personal hygiene	£8
Cleaning products	£6
Other	£3

➤ Method

❶ <u>Add</u> up the amounts.
❷ Calculate 360° ÷ ❶.
❸ <u>Multiply</u> each amount by ❷.
❹ <u>Check</u> the angles add to 360°.
❺ <u>Draw and label</u> the sectors.

Answer

❶ The total amount is £60.

❷ 360 ÷ 60 = 6

Item	Amount	Angle ❸
Food	£31	31 × 6 = 186°
Drinks	£12	12 × 6 = 72°
Personal hygiene	£8	8 × 6 = 48°
Cleaning products	£6	6 × 6 = 36°
Other	£3	3 × 6 = 18°
Total	£60	360° ❹

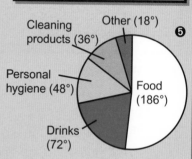

Cleaning products (36°) — Other (18°) ❺ — Personal hygiene (48°) — Food (186°) — Drinks (72°)

Tip: when using a 180° protractor, it is often easier to draw the small angles first.

● Reading pie charts

➤ Q & A (2)

Out of 30 students, how many watched BBC?

Answer

The BBC sector is 120°.

It is $\frac{120°}{360°} = \frac{1}{3}$ of the chart.

$\frac{1}{3}$ of 30 = 30 ÷ 3 = 10 students watched BBC.

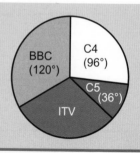

BBC (120°) — C4 (96°) — C5 (36°) — ITV

---

1 Show these colours on a pie chart:
   Red 40, Blue 25, Green 15, Other 10
2 Look at **Q & A (2)**. How many watched the other channels?

TEST

Scatter graphs

● Plotting scatter graphs

This table shows some students' results for two maths tests.

Test 1	5	8	9	11	15	17	19
Test 2	5	9	12	14	16	18	20

You can plot the points on a graph – this is a scatter graph.

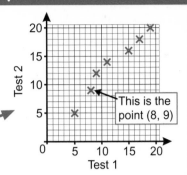

This is the point (8, 9)

● Line of best fit

This is a line drawn on a scatter graph that shows the general direction of the points.

You should try to get the same number of points above the line as below.

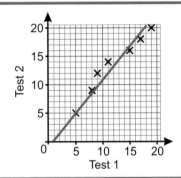

● Correlation

This is a fancy way of saying whether the points are related or not:

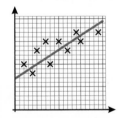

Positive correlation (/)
Strong if the points lie close to a straight line, otherwise weak.

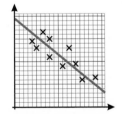

Negative correlation (\)
Strong if the points lie close to a straight line, otherwise weak.

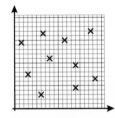

No correlation
The points seem to be randomly positioned.

Show the data as a scatter diagram.
Describe the correlation.

Age (years)	1	6	4	4	10	3	8	7	9
Value (£)	45	18	28	24	4	37	10	17	9

TEST

Probability (1)

Probability is to do with the chance of something happening.

You can use words to describe different probabilities, such as: *impossible, very unlikely, unlikely, evens, likely, very likely, certain.*

Probabilities can also be given as fractions or decimals, but they are always between 0 and 1. If something has probability 0 it can't happen; if it has probability 1 it will definitely happen.

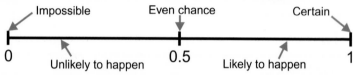

Impossible   Even chance   Certain

0   0.5   1

Unlikely to happen   Likely to happen

● Probability of something NOT happening

If the probability of something happening is p, then the probability of it not happening = $1 - p$.

> ➤ The probability of it raining tomorrow is 0.3, so the probability of it not raining tomorrow is $1 - 0.3 = 0.7$.

● Listing the outcomes of two (or more) events

➤ **Q & A**

A coin is tossed and a dice thrown. List the possible outcomes.

Answer

There are 2 possible outcomes for the coin: Heads (H) or Tails (T). For the dice there are 6 possible outcomes: 1, 2, 3, 4, 5 or 6.

List the outcomes systematically starting with Heads (H):

H1, H2, H3, H4, H5, H6
T1, T2, T3, T4, T5, T6 ← H6 is short for Heads and a 6.

Toby is going to choose a main course and dessert from the menu.

Main course	Dessert
Spaghetti	Fruit pie
Pizza	Ice cream
	Trifle

a List the possible outcomes for Toby's meal.

b The probability of Toby choosing pizza is 0.65. What is the probability that Toby doesn't choose pizza?

TEST

 Speedy Revision

Probability (2)

● Calculating probabilities

> Probability of an event = $\dfrac{\text{Number of ways an event can happen}}{\text{Total number of possible outcomes}}$

➤ Q & A

You throw a fair dice. What is the probability of getting:
a a 6   **b** an even number?

Answer

When throwing a dice there are 6 possible outcomes: 1, 2, 3, 4, 5, 6

a   There is only one way of getting a 6.   P(6) is a short way of writing
   P(6) = $\frac{1}{6}$ 'the probability of getting 6'.

b   There are 3 ways of getting an even number: 2, 4 or 6.
   P(even) = $\frac{3}{6}$ = $\frac{1}{2}$ Use the formula!

● Experimental probability

You can estimate probabilities from experimental data.
For example, the table shows the results when a spinner was spun
100 times:

Colour	Red	Black	Grey
Frequency	35	60	5

From the table, you can estimate that the probability that the
spinner lands on black is $\frac{60}{100}$ = $\frac{3}{5}$.

> Theoretical and experimental probabilities should be similar,
> but are unlikely to be the same.

For example, if you toss a coin 100 times and get heads 48 times,
you shouldn't think that the coin is unfair (biased).
Increasing the number of times an experiment is repeated generally
leads to better estimates of probability.

---

1   Use a word(s) to descibe the probability that the next baby born at
   your local hospital will be a girl.
2   A bag contains 2 red and 4 green beads. A bead is drawn from the
   bag at random. What is the probability that the bead is red?

TEST

Speedy revision test (1)

These questions test the basic facts. The simple truth is that the more of them you can answer, the better you'll do in your SATs. So try them as often as you can. (The answers can be found on the pages given at the end of each question.)

1. What are the first five square, triangular and prime numbers? (p4)
2. What is a multiple? What is a factor? (p5)
3. Write 20 as a product of its prime factors. (p5)
4. How do you find the LCM of two numbers? How about the HCF? (p6)
5. How far, and which way, should the digits move when dividing by 1000? (p7)
6. Round 0.168 to two decimal places. (p8)
7. Round 5384 to two significant figures. (p9)
8. The denominator is the top of the fraction. True or false? (p10)
9. Write $\frac{15}{45}$ in its simplest form. (p10)
10. Work out **a** $\frac{2}{3} + \frac{1}{5}$ **b** $\frac{3}{4} \times \frac{5}{7}$ **c** $\frac{2}{9} \div \frac{3}{7}$. (pp10–11)
11. Express £26 as a percentage of £40. (p12)
12. Increase £20 by 17.5%. (p12)
13. Write these as fractions: **a** 75% **b** 0.12 (p13)
14. What should you do first when ordering fractions, decimals & percentages? (p14)
15. Simplify the ratio 50 : 100. (p14)
16. Divide £120 in the ratio 2 : 3. (p15)
17. Five apples cost 90p. How much would eight apples cost? (p15)
18. Which of these is correct: $-10 < -5$ or $-10 > -5$? (p16)
19. Work out **a** $-3 + 5$ **b** $-1 - 7$. (p16)
20. What is any non-zero number to the power of zero? (p17)
21. What is any number to the power of one? (p17)
22. What is six to the power of minus one? (p17)
23. What are the missing words? (p18)
    To multiply powers of the same number you _____ the indices.
    To divide powers of the same number you _____ the indices.
    To take the power of a power you _____ the indices.
24. Write 0.0045 in standard form. (p19)
25. Write 2.3×10^{-5} as a normal number. (p19)
26. What does the standard form button look like on your calculator? (p20)
27. Use written methods to find **a** $57.3 - 1.28$ **b** 7.18×9 **c** $105.7 \div 7$ (pp20–21)
28. What does BIDMAS stand for? Work out $5^2 - 2 \times (7 - 3)$. (p22)
29. In algebra, what is a 'term'? What is an 'expression'? (p23)
30. Work out $\frac{x}{3} + \frac{4x}{3}$. (p23)
31. Multiply out the brackets: **a** $a(4a + b)$ **b** $-3(c - d)$ **c** $(a + 3)(a - 2)$ (p24)
32. Solve $7x - 4 = 10$. (p25)
33. Given that $y = 4x^3$, work out the value of y when $x = 2$. (p26)
34. What does 'making x the subject of a formula' mean? (p27)
35. Find the nth term of these: **a** 6, 10, 14, 18, ... **b** 2, 5, 10, 17, ... (p29)
36. Find the inverse function of $x \rightarrow 2x + 4$. (p30)
37. What should you construct before drawing a graph? (p32)
38. How do you work out the gradient of a line? (p33)

Speedy revision test (2)

39 How do you know if the gradient is positive or negative? (p33)

40 In '$y = mx + c$', what do m and c tell you? (p33)

41 Is the line $y = b$ vertical or horizontal? (p33)

42 What does the gradient in a distance–time graph tell you? (p34)

43 What are the four inequality symbols, and what do they mean? (p35)

44 When showing inequalities on a number line, what do ○ and ● mean? (p35)

45 What should you do first when answering a trial & improvement question? (p36)

46 Roughly how many kilometres are there in a mile? (p37)

47 What do the angles on a straight line add up to? Angles at a point? (p40)

48 Draw diagrams to show **a** vertically opposite angles **b** alternate angles **c** corresponding angles. (p40)

49 What do the angles in a triangle add up to? What about a quadrilateral? (p41)

50 What are the two formulae concerning interior and exterior angles? (p41)

51 What is special about a *regular* polygon? (p41)

52 If a shape can be folded so that one half fits exactly on the other, what is it said to have? (p42)

53 What is the order of rotation symmetry of a square? (p42 or p43)

54 When you reflect a shape in a mirror line what are not changed? (p44)

55 Fill in the blanks. A translation moves a shape:
  ❶ a specific distance _____ or _____
  ❷ and then a specific distance _____ or _____. (p46)

56 Complete: To describe an enlargement you give its _____ and ____ ____. (p47)

57 What should you do first when working out the perimeter of a shape? (p48)

58 What is the formula for the circumference of a circle? What is π? (p48)

59 Give the formulae for the area of a triangle, rectangle, parallelogram, trapezium and circle. (pp49–50)

60 Give the formulae for the arc length and sector area of a circle. (p51)

61 What are the two circle theorems you should know? (p51)

62 What is Pythagoras' theorem? (p52)

63 Sketch nets of a cuboid and a regular tetrahedron. (p54)

64 Give the formulae for the volume of a cuboid, prism and cylinder. (p55)

65 What are the three things you should know about bearings? (p57)

66 Sketch the formula triangles for speed and density. (p58)

67 How do you work out the mean, median, mode and range? (p61)

68 What is discrete data? What is continuous data? (p62)

69 Which group does 20 belong to: $10 \leqslant n < 20$ or $20 \leqslant n < 30$? (p64)

70 How do you estimate the mean from a grouped frequency table? (p65)

71 What is the group with the highest frequency called? (p65)

72 Joining the middle of the tops of the bars in a frequency diagram gives what? (p66)

73 What is a line graph good at showing? (p67)

74 Sketch a scatter graph that shows negative correlation. (p69)

75 If the probability of an event happening is p, what's the probability of it not happening? (p70)

76 What is the formula for calculating the probability of an event happening? (p71)

TEST answers

Page 4 Special numbers
1 **a** 2, 4, 6, 8, 10, 12, 14, 16, 18, 20
   b 1, 3, 5, 7, 9, 11, 13, 15, 17, 19
   c 1, 4, 9, 16, 25, 36, 49, 64, 81, 100
   d 1, 3, 6, 10, 15, 21, 28, 36, 45, 55
2 **a** 32, 36, 64 **b** 49, 17, 21, 3 **c** 49, 36, 64
   d 21, 36, 3 **e** 17, 3

Page 5 Multiples, factors & prime factors
1 **a** 5, 10, 15, 20, 25 **b** 8, 16, 24, 32, 40
   c 6, 12, 18, 24, 30 **d** 9, 18, 27, 36, 45
2 **a** 1, 2, 4, 8 **b** 1, 2, 4, 8, 16, 32
   c 1, 2, 4, 5, 8, 10, 20, 40
3 **a** $2 \times 2 \times 3 \times 3 = 2^2 \times 3^2$
   b $2 \times 2 \times 3 \times 7 = 2^2 \times 3 \times 7$

Page 6 LCM & HCF
1 **a** 24 **b** 144
2 **a** 4 **b** 7

Page 7 Multiplying & dividing by 10, 100, ...
1 **a** 390 **b** 8000 **c** 0.71 **d** 150
   e 42 **f** 64 **g** 163 **h** 14 900
2 **a** 2400 **b** 0.024 **c** 84 000 **d** 0.7

Page 9 Rounding (2)
1 27 900, 2900, 100
2 0.58, 0.02, 12.88
3 350, 1.0, 0.81
4 **a** 5 **b** 1000

Page 10 Fractions (1)
1 $\frac{5}{8}$
2 **a** $\frac{2}{3}$ **b** $\frac{3}{4}$ **c** $\frac{2}{5}$
3 **a** $\frac{8}{9}$ **b** $\frac{1}{8}$
4 $\frac{5}{3}$
5 $3\frac{1}{3}$

Page 11 Fractions (2)
1 **a** $\frac{10}{49}$ **b** $\frac{2}{3}$ **c** $\frac{1}{3}$ **d** $\frac{9}{14}$ **e** £22

Page 12 Percentages
1 20% **2** £42 **3** **a** £1200 **b** £190

Page 13 Fractions, decimals & percentages (1)
1 **a** $\frac{11}{100}$ **b** $\frac{5}{100} = \frac{1}{20}$ **c** $\frac{6}{10} = \frac{3}{5}$ **d** $\frac{15}{100} = \frac{3}{20}$
2 **a** 0.7 **b** 70%
3 $\frac{35}{100} = \frac{7}{20}$

Page 14 Fractions, decimals & percentages (2)
145%, 3.45, $4\frac{1}{8}$, 4.2

Page 15 Ratio & proportion (2)
1 **a** 1 : 6 **b** 9 : 5 **c** 350 : 3
2 240 ml : 560 ml
3 £6.75

Page 16 Negative numbers
1 −10 **2** −5, −4, 0, 2, 3
3 **a** −8 + 3 = −5

   b −2 − 3 = −5

Page 18 Powers & roots (2)
1 **a** 144 **b** 64 **c** 32 **d** 1 **e** 100 **f** $\frac{1}{100} = 0.01$
2 **a** 6 **b** 8 **c** 10 **d** 3
3 **a** 7^7 **b** 2^5 **c** 5^{24}

Page 19 Standard index form (1)
1 **a** 3.45×10^2 **b** 2.4×10^{-4}
   c 4.5×10^4 **d** 7.64×10^8
2 **a** 3700 **b** 0.000 1 2

Page 21 Written methods (2)
1 **a** 7.89 **b** 3.54 **c** 0.16 **d** 165.831
2 **a** 828 **b** 1694 **c** 44.94
3 **a** 12.7 **b** 13.4 **c** 21.6

Page 22 Calculations with brackets
a 7 **b** 36.4 **c** 7 **d** 2

Page 23 Using letters
1 **a** $3t$ **b** $4n$ **c** $3y$ **d** $4x + 2$
2 **a** $\frac{6x}{5}$ **b** $\frac{3}{d}$

Page 24 Brackets
a $4x + 8$ **b** $mn + 7m$ **c** $a^2 + ab$ **d** $-4d + 20$
e $x^2 + 5x + 6$ **f** $x^2 - 3x - 10$ **g** $x^2 + 2x + 1$

Page 25 Equations
1 **a** $x = 3$ **b** $x = 8$
2 **❶** $x = 4$ **❷** $x = 2$ **a** $x = 2$ **b** $x = 2$

Page 26 Formulae & substitution
1 $C = 25h$ **2** £200 **3** **a** $a = 11$ **b** $a = 19$

Page 27 Rearranging formulae
1 **a** $q = \frac{\sqrt{p}}{2}$ **b** $q = \frac{\sqrt{p}}{9}$
2 **a** $a = 1 - 3b$ **b** $a = 2b$

Page 28 Sequences & number patterns (1)
1 **a** 17 **b** 48 **c** 5
2 14
3 **a** 7 **b** 105 **c** 205

Page 29 Sequences & number patterns (2)
a $3n + 4$ **b** $4n - 3$ **c** $n^2 + 3$

TEST answers

Page 30 Functions & mappings
1 **a** 22 **b** 2 **c** $x \to 5x + 2$
2 **a** $x \to 10 - x$
b The function and its inverse are the same.

Page 31 Coordinates
P(4, 2), Q(−3, 1), R(−3, −2), S(2, −2)

Page 32 Straight-line graphs (1)
a

x	−2	−1	0	1	2
$y = 3x + 2$	−4	−1	2	5	8

b
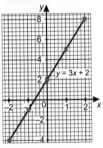

Page 33 Straight-line graphs (2)
$y = 5x + 4$

Page 34 Real-life graphs
1 The train starts at station A and travels to station C at a constant speed. The train waits at station C before travelling to station B. The train waits at station B and then travels more slowly back to station A.
2 5

Page 36 Inequalities
1 **a** −4, −3, −2, −1, 0, 1
b
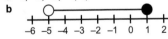

2 **a** $x < 2$
b
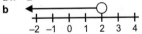

Page 36 Trial & improvement
$x = 3.77$

Page 37 Units of measurement
1 **a** 200 cm **b** 6 cm
2 **a** Roughly 30 g **b** Roughly 450 g

Page 38 Reading scales & accuracy
1 **a** 35 **b** 68
2 **a** 13.5 kg, 14.5 kg **b** 2.95 cm, 3.05 cm

Page 39 Estimating & measuring angles
1 **a** Between 70° & 80° **b** Between 160° & 170°
2 **a** 75° **b** 165°

Page 40 Angles & parallel lines
$a = 65°$, $b = 56°$, $c = d = 124°$, $e = 38°$, $f = 128°$

Page 41 Polygons
1 49°
2 **a** Interior = 90°, exterior = 90°
b Interior = 120°, exterior = 60°

Page 43 Symmetry & properties of shapes (2)
1 **a i** 2 **ii** 2 **b i** 1 **ii** 1 **c i** 3 **ii** 3
2 For example:

Page 44 Reflection
a

b
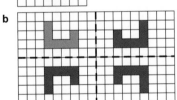

Page 45 Rotation
a

b
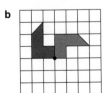

TEST answers

Page 46 Translation

1

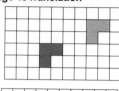

2

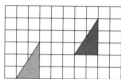

Page 47 Enlargement

1

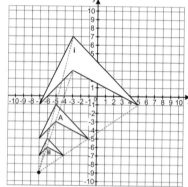

2 **a** Enlargement with centre $(-1, 1)$, s.f. $\frac{1}{2}$

b Enlargement with centre $(7, -3)$, s.f. 2

Page 48 Perimeter & circumference

1 **a** 28 cm **b** 28 cm

2 50.24 cm (using $\pi = 3.14$)

Page 49 Areas of triangles & quadrilaterals

a 42 cm² **b** 33 cm² **c** 18 cm² **d** 27 m²

Page 50 Areas of circles & composite shapes

a 153.86 cm² (using $\pi = 3.14$) **b** 122.5 cm²

Page 51 More circles

a 6.28 cm to 2 d.p. **b** 9.42 cm² to 2 d.p.

Page 53 Pythagoras' theorem (2)

1 **a** 12.5 cm **b** 12.1 cm **c** 19.6 km

2 **a** 10.6 units **b** 19.2 units

3 **a** (7.5, 9) **b** (18, 3.5)

Page 54 Nets & 3-D shapes; plans & elevations

1 **a** 6 faces, 12 edges, 8 vertices

b 5 faces, 9 edges, 6 vertices

2 For example:

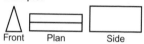

Front   Plan   Side

The 11 nets of a cube are:

Page 56 Volume & surface area (2)

1 **a** 600 m³, 660 m² **b** 126 m³, 152.4 m²

c 2261.9 cm³, 980.2 cm² (curved surface is a rectangle, width same as circumference)

2 **a** 6×10^8 cm³, 6.6×10^6 cm²

c 0.002 261 9 m³, 0.098 02 m²

Page 57 Bearings & scale drawings

1 **a** 090° **b** 270° **2** 100 km

Page 58 Compound measures

1 40 minutes

2 1000 kg

Page 60 Constructions & loci (2)

3

Ends should be semicircles

Page 61 Mean, median, mode, range (1)

Mode = 4, median = 5, mean = 6, range = 8

Page 62 Discrete & continous data

a Continuous **b** Discrete

TEST answers

Page 63 Collecting data & two-way tables

1 There is no option for 1 dog.

2

	Black	Red	Blue	Total
Boys own	14	**1**	11	26
Girls own	7	7	**20**	34
Total	21	8	31	60

Page 64 Frequency tables (1)

Number, n	Tally	Frequency
$0 \leqslant n < 10$	III	3
$10 \leqslant n < 20$	III	3
$20 \leqslant n < 30$	III	3
$30 \leqslant n < 40$	₩	5
$40 \leqslant n < 50$	II	2
Total		16

Page 65 Frequency tables (2)

a

Height (h cm)	Tally	Frequency
$150 \leqslant h < 155$	I	1
$155 \leqslant h < 160$	IIII	4
$160 \leqslant h < 165$	III	3
$165 \leqslant h < 170$	₩ III	8
$170 \leqslant h < 175$	II	2
$175 \leqslant h < 180$	II	2

b 3310 ÷ 20 = 165.5 cm (midpoints: 152.5, etc)
c $165 \leqslant h < 170$ **d** $165 \leqslant h < 170$

Page 66 Bar charts & frequency diagrams

a

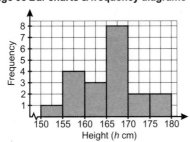

b

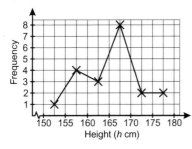

Page 67 Stem & leaf diagrams; line graphs

1

4	2 8 9
5	0 1 4 6 7 8 8 9
6	0 2 2 2 2 3 3 5 7 8 9 9
7	0 0 2 2 3 4 5

Key: 1│8 means 18

2 The number of students being late falls as each week goes along, but more students were late in the second week.

Page 68 Pie charts

1

2 ITV: 9 students
C4: 8 students
C5: 3 students

Page 69 Scatter graphs

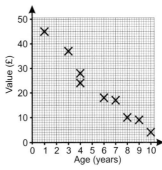

The graph shows strong negative correlation, i.e. value decreases as age increases.

Page 70 Probability (1)

a spaghetti & fruit pie, pizza & fruit pie
spaghetti & ice cream, pizza & ice cream
spaghetti & trifle, pizza & trifle
b 0.35

Page 71 Probability (2)

1 Evens, even chance or fifty-fifty
2 $\frac{2}{6} = \frac{1}{3}$

Index

Index

Index

Speedy Revision